S0-AIW-299

an introduction to the
ORGANIC CHEMISTRY
OF HIGH POLYMERS

by CARL S. MARVEL

Research Professor of Organic Chemistry
University of Illinois

NEW YORK · JOHN WILEY & SONS, INC.

London · Chapman & Hall, Limited

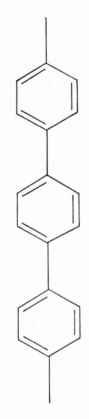

an introduction to the
ORGANIC CHEMISTRY
OF HIGH POLYMERS

53757

547.84
M 39

Copyright © 1959 by John Wiley & Sons, Inc.

All Rights Reserved. This book or any part
thereof must not be reproduced in any form
without the written permission of the publisher.

Library of Congress Catalog Card Number: 59-14991
Printed in the United States of America

Preface

These notes were originally assembled for use in connection with the Humble Lectures in Science delivered by me in June of 1956. They have since found use as a means of interesting young organic chemists in the possibilities inherent in the synthesis of new organic polymers. They are now being reproduced to make this use more widespread. They are intended for the beginner in polymer synthesis and are not designed to be comprehensive in their coverage.

I am indebted to a number of my faculty colleagues and current and former students for helpful criticism of these notes.

C. S. M.

Urbana, Illinois
September, 1959

Contents

Introduction

High molecular weight materials such as the proteins, rubber, and cellulose have been of interest to chemists for a very long time. These substances have been known to have unusual properties not exhibited by smaller molecules. Most early investigators thought these materials consisted of units held together by bonds different from the types of valence which are operative in the common molecules with which the organic chemist works. Some individuals did try to point out the polymeric (as now defined) nature of some of the materials as long ago as 1871,[1] but their view was not generally accepted until about 1930.

In an important paper published in 1920 [2] Staudinger specifically proposed chain formulas for polystyrene and polyoxymethylene and decried the prevailing tendency to consider high molecular weight substances as being held together by some variety of partial valences

$$—CH_2—CH—CH_2—CH— \qquad —CH_2O—CH_2O—CH_2O—$$
$$\qquad\quad | \qquad\quad\; |$$
$$\qquad\quad C_6H_5 \qquad C_6H_5$$

rather than by normal valence bonds. Staudinger did not attempt to assign end groups to his molecules, but he did emphasize that these molecules were not likely to be cyclic. Staudinger continued to support the idea of macromolecules in his later papers.

Others gradually began to support Staudinger's views. K. Meyer

[1] H. Hlasiwetz and J. Habermann, *Ann. Chem. Pharm.*, **159**, 304 (1871).
[2] H. Staudinger, *Ber.*, **53**, 1073 (1920).

and H. Mark were among his early advocates. It was in 1929 that Carothers [3] published his first work on synthetic polymers. His investigations were especially successful in establishing the true nature of the valence forces in macromolecules and in dispelling the mysticism which up to then had prevailed in this field. He introduced the idea of functionality in monomer molecules and gave sound definitions which clarified the thinking of others.

Staudinger and Carothers thus are the two men who have done the most to place polymer chemistry on a sound chemical foundation.

Definitions

Berzelius [4] first introduced the term polymer to recognize the fact that two compounds may have the same composition but different molecular weights. Gradually chemists have come to accept this term as applying to materials in which this condition is not strictly maintained.

Carothers [5] introduced the idea that *polymerization* is a reaction which is functionally capable of proceeding indefinitely and described polymers in terms of their *recurring structural units*. In his view polymerization covered the combination of a number of similar molecules to form a single molecule. A polymer was any substance produced by this process or degraded by a reverse process.

Polyoxymethylene and polyethylene sebacate are examples of the polymerization of what Carothers called difunctional molecules; such polymers were called *linear polymers*. The *degree of polymerization* is the number of recurring structural units (n in these formulas) in the final macromolecule. The structural units are related to the monomer structures. In polyoxymethylene the recurring structural unit is only 2 atoms long. In polyethylene sebacate the structural unit contains

---

[3] W. H. Carothers, *J. Am. Chem. Soc.*, **51**, 2548 (1929).

[4] J. J. Berzelius, *Jahres-Bericht*, **12**, 63 (1833).

[5] W. H. Carothers, *Chem. Revs.*, **8**, 353–426 (1931).

$$nCH_2{=}O \xrightarrow{H_2O} HO{-}(CH_2O)_n{-}H$$

Polyoxymethylene

both the acid and glycol fragments. The nature of the end groups be-

$$nHOCH_2CH_2OH + nHOOC(CH_2)_8COOH \longrightarrow H{-}[OCO(CH_2)_8{-}COOCH_2CH_2]_n OH +$$

Polyethylene sebacate

$$2nH_2O$$

came important to Carothers, who did not believe that the end groups could be ignored. The end groups in the cases above are indicated to be H and OH. In the first example the end groups come from an added molecule and not from the monomer. In the second example the end groups are parts of the monomer units. Polyethylene sebacate is still capable of further self-reaction because it has terminal hydroxyl and carboxyl groups. Actually there may be accidental side reactions which destroy these end groups and thus terminate the growth of the polymer.

It might be well to digress briefly at this point to note that a polymer is named on the basis of the recurring unit with the prefix "poly" combined with the name or the first word in the name of the monomer. The following are examples.

$$-(CH_2CH_2)_n$$

Polyethylene

$$-(CH_2O)_n$$

Polyoxymethylene

$$H{-}[OCO(CH_2)_8COOCH_2CH_2]_n OH$$

Polyethylene sebacate

$$\left(CH_2{-}\underset{\underset{CO_2CH_3}{|}}{CH}\right)$$

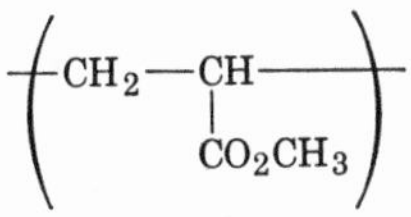

Polymethyl acrylate

Carothers [5] further classified polymerization reactions as *condensation polymerization* and *addition polymerization*. In condensation polymerization, represented above by the esterification of a dibasic acid by a dihydroxy alcohol, there is the loss of a simple molecule, water, as each recurring structural unit in the polymer is introduced. Hence the condensation polymer does not have the same composition as the monomer molecules. The polymer may be degraded to the monomers by the reversal of its formation in these instances.

In addition polymerization the molecular formula of the recurring structural unit is identical with the monomer from which it is produced. Even here the polymer does not have the exact composition of the monomer because some end groups must be introduced (as the case of formaldehyde).

When molecules with a functionality of more than two are used in polymer-forming reactions, the polymer may be *branched* or *crosslinked,* depending on the extent of polyfunctionality, the ratios of reactants used, and the degree of polymerization. The well-known glycerol-phthalic anhydride reaction and the phenol-formaldehyde reaction lead to highly crosslinked structures. Instead of such highly crosslinked polymers, branched molecules can be obtained by decreasing the extent of polyfunctionality. Cyclization sometimes occurs to decrease crosslinking and branching.

It is characteristic of crosslinked materials that they are extremely insoluble. Branched polymers vary in this respect according to their complexity.

Flory [6] points out that the really significant difference between condensation and addition polymers (and polymerizations) lies in the differences in the processes by which they are produced. In general, a condensation polymer is formed by step-wise reactions of two groups with the loss of the small molecule.

It should be emphasized that the chemistry of the formation of condensation polymers is the simple organic chemistry used in making low molecular weight materials. Such reactions as esterification and amide formation are extensively used. The condensation polymers will be composed of a mixture of materials in which the degree of polymerization varies. These polymers, then, are different in their properties from crystalline monomeric materials. Polymers often have crystalline regions, but it is rare for a polymer to be 100% crystalline. Usually, either solubility of polymers is complete or the polymer does not dissolve at all. It is not likely that a polymer ever will be recrystallized by dissolving it in a hot solvent and having it separate on cooling. Since our only methods of purification are solution in a solvent and pouring the solution into a non-solvent or by extraction of soluble impurities with a polymer non-solvent, we usually try to make the polymers from very pure monomer so the contamination of the polymeric material is as low as possible.

[6] P. J. Flory, *Principles of Polymer Chemistry,* Cornell University Press, Ithaca, N. Y., 1953, p. 38.

In the case of addition polymers the most common materials are prepared from olefins by ionic or radical chain reactions which are quite different from the ordinary reactions of classical organic chemistry. Here we have olefin monomer and then high polymer. There are no intermediate stages under ordinary conditions.

We now have some interesting cases which are borderline in this sense. By Carothers' definition they might be strictly addition polymers, but because of their step-wise formation Flory believes they more properly should be considered with condensation polymers. Thus, for a glycol-diisocyanate reaction, we have a step-wise reaction

$$\text{HOROH} + \text{O=C=N—R'—N=C=O} \longrightarrow \text{HO}\left(\text{R—O—}\overset{\overset{\text{O}}{\|}}{\text{C}}\text{—}\underset{\underset{\text{H}}{|}}{\text{N}}\text{—R'}\right)\text{NCO}$$

similar to polyesterification in which the process is addition, but not the chain type reaction characteristic of vinyl polymerization.

The conversion of a cyclic monomer such as lactide to a linear polymer is another borderline case which is more probably a chain type reaction than a step-wise addition. Further cases will be con-

$$\text{CH}_3\text{—CH}\overset{\text{O}}{\underset{\text{CO}}{<}}\overset{\text{CO}}{\underset{\text{O}}{>}}\text{CH—CH}_3 \quad \xrightarrow{\text{H}_2\text{O}} \quad \text{H}\left(\text{O—}\overset{\overset{\text{CH}_3}{|}}{\text{CH}}\text{—CO}\right)_n\text{OH}$$

sidered as we go into the treatment of specific examples. Although there are such mixed cases, the usefulness of the Carothers concept still holds in a general way, and no better classification has been devised.

Inorganic Polymers

It should be pointed out that the ability to form long chain molecules is not limited to organic substances, although as yet the organic materials have the greatest practical utility. Polymers of $-\text{PCl}_2\text{N}-$ and $-\text{S}_x-$, which are rubbery, have been described. Sulfur trioxide gives a fibrous polymer. Some of the complex silicates are probably properly included among the crosslinked polymers.

Copolymers

In the addition polymers from vinyl type monomers we have examples of two different vinyl monomers entering the chain to produce a polymer in which there are two different recurring units distributed along the chain in more or less random fashion. Such polymers are usually called copolymers, although sometimes the term interpolymers has been preferred. Usually the term copolymer has been limited to the vinyl field, although it seems proper to think of copolymers of the polyester type in which two dibasic acids and one glycol, two glycols and one dibasic acid or even more ingredients, have been used in the polyesterification.

Characterization of Polymers

Before taking up the chemistry of polymer formation and reactions it seems desirable to discuss very briefly the methods used to characterize polymers. Polymers differ from the ordinary molecules of the organic chemist because they cannot be distilled and usually cannot be purified by recrystallization. They consist of mixtures of like molecules of varying molecular weights which differ from each other by some multiple of the weight of the recurring unit. It is less simple to characterize these materials than it is to characterize monomers. It becomes a research job to determine molecular weight, density, refractive index, melting point, and other properties for a polymer.

One of the important determinations on a polymer is that of finding its molecular weight. Many of the physical properties of a polymer are closely related to the size of the molecule, and in practical work all these properties are significant. It is always important to know whether a given sample is greater or less in molecular weight than another of the same type.

The classical methods of molecular weight determination such as freezing point lowering and boiling point raising are applicable only to very low molecular weight polymers. Osmotic pressure methods are used successfully but the determination is time consuming. Often this method is used as a standard for other methods.

One chemical method of determining molecular weight has been the use of end group analysis. This does require that one know the number and kind of end groups (two or one in a linear polymer). It is also necessary to be as certain as possible that all the polymeric molecules in the sample have the same end groups. This is not an easy assignment. If branching occurs in polymer growth, the end group method fails. In such molecules as polyesters the terminal

$$-\overset{\overset{\displaystyle O}{\displaystyle \parallel}}{C}-OH$$ group can be titrated. The method becomes increasingly insensitive as the molecular weight becomes greater. It has been used principally in the molecular weight range of 15,000 to 25,000 which is fairly common in condensation polymers.

In recent years new methods of molecular weight determination by measurements of light scattering, sedimentation equilibrium, and sedimentation velocity in conjunction with diffusion have come into use. These are all absolute methods of determining molecular weight and hence valuable. They are also often time consuming and require experts to use them accurately. They need to be applied to very dilute solutions.

In practice, molecular weights are determined by viscosity measurements. This is not an absolute method but requires standardization with other methods. Once this standardization has been made on a given type of polymer, the method has accuracy great enough to be useful in research. Flory [7] prefers standardization by light scattering to that by osmotic measurements.

It is important to remember that polymer samples are *almost invariably* rather complex mixtures of macromolecules of various sizes. In most of the molecular weight methods based on a study of colligative properties of solutions, one determines the number of soluble molecules rather than their size. This is called the "number average" molecular weight and represents the actual weight of the polymer sample divided by the actual number of molecules it contains. The equation which defines the term is

$$M_n = \frac{\Sigma N_i M_i}{\Sigma N_i}$$

End group analyses always give number average molecular weights. Number average molecular weights are sensitive to small weight fractions of low molecular weight constituents and relatively insensitive to small weight proportions of high molecular weight molecules.

Light scattering methods of determining molecular weight tend to

[7] *Ibid.,* p. 314.

measure weights of particles rather than mere numbers of particles in the solution. The molecular weight of a polymer obtained by this and related methods has been termed "weight average" molecular weight, and it is defined by the equation

$$M_w = \frac{\Sigma N_i M_i^2}{\Sigma N_i M_i}$$

This molecular weight figure is sensitive to the presence of larger species of molecules and hence is higher than the number average molecular weight for polymers with a considerable distribution in molecular sizes. For a random distribution, the weight average molecular weight is twice the number average molecular weight. If equal parts by weight of molecules $M = 10,000$ and $M = 100,000$ are mixed together, the mixture will show a number average molecular weight of 18,200 and a weight average molecular weight of 55,000. If equal number of molecules are mixed for these two polymers, the number average molecular weight will be 55,000 and the weight average molecular weight will be 92,000.

Intrinsic viscosity molecular weights are calculated by the equation $[\eta] = K'M^a$. K and a are constants that have to be determined by comparing intrinsic viscosities of a series of polymers against osmotic or light scattering molecular weights in standard solvents. The equation is an empirical one, but once the value of K and a are determined it is a fairly satisfactory equation to use for molecular weight calculations. Depending on the absolute method of molecular weight used to determine K and a, the viscosity molecular weight will be essentially number average or weight average.

For a thorough discussion of these methods of determining molecular weights and the mathematical derivations and interrelations one should consult a treatment such as that in Flory's *Principles of Polymer Chemistry*.[6]

The molecular weight distribution is an important factor in determining the properties of a polymer. To determine this distribution with any degree of accuracy is still a difficult undertaking. Some estimate of the distribution can be made by comparing number average and weight average molecular weights. The best semiquantitative results have come from fractionation studies, but these are approximations because they depend on differential solubilities which are slight at best. Sedimentation equilibrium and sedimentation velocity measurements have been discussed as methods but have not actually been developed as routine laboratory procedures.

Flory has decided that statistical considerations may be best used to estimate the probable distribution of molecular weight in a polymer, and he develops this idea in his book.[6]

For the practical polymer chemist the fractionation method is still the best one available for determining the molecular weight distribution, and it is not highly satisfactory. It is usually true that a narrow distribution range seems to give more useful polymers.

In polymer work we are usually interested in the melting or softening point (transition point) and the tensile strength of the polymer. These properties are related to molecular size and shape. Low molecular weight polymers are nearly always lower melting than higher molecular weight polymers in a given series. Also, low molecular weight polymers are likely to be brittle and of poor strength whereas higher molecular weight polymers are tough and strong. These generalizations must be related to the structure of the polymer in question. The interchain attractions between various types of polymers vary and affect their physical properties greatly. However, melting point and tensile strength in a given series can usually be represented in a plot such as the accompanying one. That is, at lower molecular

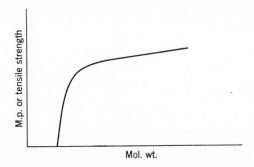

weights the melting point and the tensile strength are very much affected by the molecular weight. But, after a certain size of molecule is reached, there is very little further increase in either with increased size of the molecule. Where the break in properties comes is determined by the nature of the polymer.

For example, in a polyhydrocarbon such as a synthetic polybutadiene the molecular weight must be in the 100,000 to 1,000,000 range to give a tough polymer of high tensile strength, whereas in a nylon type of polymer, which has strong hydrogen bonding forces between chains, high tensile strength and toughness can be achieved at as low as 20,000 molecular weight.

The degree of orientation of polymer chains in a sample and the extent of crystallinity of the polymer also greatly affect the properties of a polymer molecule. These properties can be changed in a given polymer by proper treatment, and such treatments become an important part of polymer technology. Usually condensation polymers are regular and tend to crystallize to a greater extent than do addition polymers from vinyl monomers. Crystalline polymers are apt to be translucent or opaque. Usually a symmetrical type of monomer unit will lead to a polymer of higher softening point than will an unsymmetrical unit. This is especially noticeable when ring systems become a part of the main polymer chain.

Polyethylene terephthalate has a much higher softening point than polyethylene isophthalate. The polymeric esters of 2,6-naphthalenedicarboxylic acid melt higher than those of 2,5-, 1,4-, or other less symmetrical monomeric arrangements.

Copolymers are less crystalline than the homopolymers because of greater irregularity. Vinyl polymers are usually much more amorphous than condensation polymers, and this has frequently been related to the stereochemistry of the molecules. Each recurring unit in most high polymers has an asymmetric carbon atom, hence the

$$-CH_2-\overset{*}{C}H-$$
$$\underset{x}{|}$$

number of theoretically possible isomers is 2^n, where n is the degree of polymerization. The greater the number of isomers, the less is the tendency to crystallize.

Another reason why vinyls are apt to lack crystallinity is that often they are branched to a greater or lesser degree. This point will be more fully discussed after we consider the mechanism of their formation.

In practice, viscosity determinations are used as one of the important steps in characterization of a polymer. Solubility is an important property of many polymers and must, of course, be determined to permit the determination of the intrinsic viscosity.

The melting point can be determined for crystalline polymers, and it is frequently a very definite characteristic. For polymers which are not highly crystalline a softening point is often determined, and it has some value in characterization. For amorphous polymers the glass temperature is a valuable constant. This is the temperature at which a hard and brittle polymer becomes viscous or rubbery. Polymer units which have strong van der Waals interactions are apt to have high glass temperatures.

X-ray patterns are important in polymer characterization, and an expert can determine the degree of crystallinity and orientation from such patterns.

Infrared absorption spectra are useful in the characterization of polymers. Many structural features can be detected by this means.

Density is another important property of polymers, and high density usually means greater linearity and regularity in a given series.

Condensation Polymerization

General Considerations

As defined above, condensation polymerization involves the reaction of a polyfunctional molecule or molecules with the loss of some simple molecule such as water or hydrogen chloride with the formation of a macromolecule. When a difunctional molecule is used, a linear condensation polymerization takes place. The condensation polymerizations which have received the most study are probably those leading to polyesters and polyamides, and these will be discussed to illustrate some of the general principles involved.

It is an important fact that the reactivity of a functional group does not seem to be affected markedly by the size of the molecule of which it is a part. Steric factors are important, as in monomer chemistry. Hence in the esterification of a dibasic acid by a dihydroxy alcohol the rate of reaction between the end groups does not slow down appreciably as the polymer increases in size. This is surprising because

$$n\text{HOCO}(CH_2)_x\text{COOH} + n\text{HOROH} \longrightarrow HO\left[\underset{\underset{O}{\parallel}}{C}-(CH_2)_x-\overset{\overset{O}{\diagup}}{C}-OR-O\right]_n H$$

we have generally come to believe that low molecular weight molecules react more rapidly. Kinetic studies have shown, however, that although there is some change in going from 1- to 5-carbon compounds the rate appears to level off with further increase in size. The rate of the polymerization reaction is more likely to be affected by the viscosity of the reaction mixture, falling off rapidly as the viscosity increases. Thus, in the polyesterification cited above, water must be lost from the reaction mixture to drive the reaction toward the right side (polymer formation). If high viscosity retards the escape of the water, the hydrolysis reaction equilibrates with esterification and the average size of the polymer molecule no longer increases. The rate of loss of water is a function of the viscosity of the reaction mixture, pressure on the mixture, temperature of the mixture, and other properties.

This may be a good place to point out the importance of using extremely pure reactants in a polymer-forming reaction. If the reaction is to be functionally capable of proceeding indefinitely, the groups which react must be paired accurately so that their rates of disappearance are identical and so that the terminal groups are still balanced in the polymer. We can make use of an off-balance treatment to limit the size of a polymer formed in a condensation reaction. If an excess of glycol is used in the polyesterification reaction written above, for example, the polymerization stops at a certain molecular weight at which the end groups are all glycol groups. Or, if an excess of acid is used, the end groups will be carboxyl and again no further polymerization will occur.

When control of the molecular weight is desired, an excess of one reagent over the other may be used, but more frequently one adds an amount of a monobasic reactant calculated so that exactly the desired molecular weight is reached. This added monofunctional reactant is called a molecular weight or viscosity stabilizer. The use of such stabilizers and the methods of calculating the amount that should be used in a specific instance are described by Coffman, Berchet, Peterson, and Spanagel.[8]

The need for using pure reagents can thus be seen. If one is preparing a polyester from a hydroxy acid, say $HO(CH_2)_6COOH$, and a molecular weight of 25,000 is desired, it will be necessary for the degree of polymerization to reach approximately 200 units. If there are present in 200 molecules of the hydroxy acid a few molecules of either an alcohol (ROH)

---

[8] D. D. Coffman, G. J. Berchet, W. R. Peterson, and E. W. Spanagel, *J. Polymer Sci.*, **2**, 306 (1947).

or an acid $\left(RC\overset{O}{\diagup}{}_{\diagdown}OH\right)$, this degree of polymerization cannot be reached.

These observations also point out the necessity of using a reaction to produce polymers which gives a nearly quantitative yield of a single species. Side reactions which destroy the balance of reacting groups will cut short polymer growth. It is safe to say that more money has been wasted in industrial research by the use of impure reagents in studying polymer-forming reactions than in almost any other way. Of course, some impurities can be tolerated if they are such that they take no part in the reaction or do not upset the balance of reacting groups.

In carrying out condensation polymerizations with difunctional molecules there is always the chance that the reaction can terminate by one end group reacting with the other end group of the same molecule to produce a cyclic compound. When five- or six-membered rings can form by this method, the cyclization reaction predominates. The ready formation of γ- and δ-lactones from the corresponding hydroxy acids or the corresponding lactams from the amino acids is well known. When the ring size is less than five or greater than six, the normal reaction is not cyclization but polymerization. Even in the latter cases some large ring compounds do form and can be isolated in small yields. By use of the Ruggli high dilution principle the ring formation can be greatly increased at the expense of polymer formation. Occasionally a large ring forms with unexpected ease. One such reaction which was described in older literature and then recently rediscovered is the mercaptal formation from an aldehyde and a dimercaptan. Thus benzaldehyde and decamethylene dimercaptan in fairly concentrated dioxane solution form the 26-membered cyclic dimercaptal in yields of more than 50%.

$$2C_6H_5C\overset{O}{\underset{H}{\diagup}} \ +2HS-(CH_2)_{10}-SH \ \rightarrow$$

$$C_6H_5-\underset{\underset{H}{|}}{C}\overset{\diagup S(CH_2)_{10}-S\diagdown}{\diagdown S(CH_2)_{10}-S}\underset{\underset{H}{|}}{C}-C_6H_5 + 2H_2O$$

In the polyesterification of ethylene glycol with terephthalic acid the cyclic dimer is obtained in low yield.

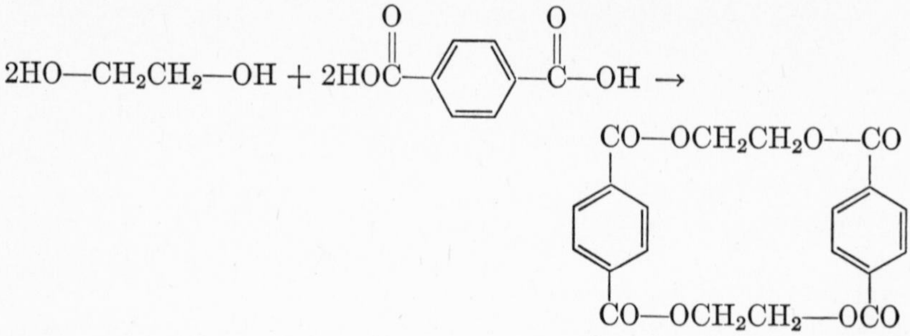

$$2HO—CH_2CH_2—OH + 2HOC \overset{O}{\underset{}{\|}} —\langle\bigcirc\rangle— \overset{O}{\underset{}{\|}} C—OH \rightarrow$$

$$
\begin{array}{c}
CO—OCH_2CH_2O—CO \\
| \qquad\qquad\qquad | \\
\langle\bigcirc\rangle \qquad\qquad \langle\bigcirc\rangle \\
| \qquad\qquad\qquad | \\
CO—OCH_2CH_2—OCO
\end{array}
$$

In the preparation of polyethylene isophthalate as much as 10 to 15% of the product is the cyclic dimer.[9]   In such reactions the cyclic material formed does not destroy the balance of end groups, and polymers of satisfactory molecular weights still may be formed.

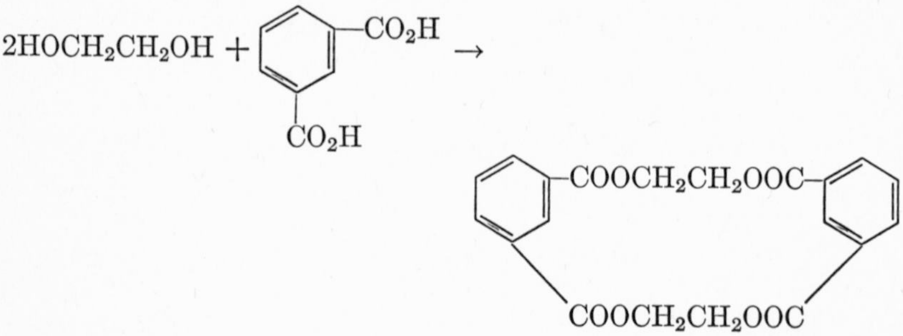

$$2HOCH_2CH_2OH + \; \langle\bigcirc\rangle\!\!\begin{array}{c} —CO_2H \\ \\ CO_2H \end{array} \; \rightarrow$$

$$
\begin{array}{c}
\langle\bigcirc\rangle\text{-}COOCH_2CH_2OOC\text{-}\langle\bigcirc\rangle \\
| \qquad\qquad\qquad\qquad | \\
COOCH_2CH_2OOC
\end{array}
$$

Polyesters

Polyesterification reactions were extensively studied by Carothers and his research group in their initial research with polymers.   The field has continued to become more and more important as more and more industrially prominent polyesters have been developed.   In this treatise the general reactions of formation rather than specific methods for producing practical polymers will be stressed.

Polyesters may be made by any method which can be used for an ordinary ester with the usual restrictions that apply to polymer formation.   The reaction must give the product in high yield and uncontaminated with by-product.   With these two points in mind we can then set down the following reactions as general for making polyesters.

[9] C. E. Burr, *J. Polymer Sci.*, **15**, 591 (1955).

1. Direct Esterification

$$n\text{HOROH} + n\text{HOCOR'COOH} \xrightarrow{\text{cat.}} \text{HO}\!-\!\!(\text{ROCOR'}\!-\!\text{CO}\!-\!\text{O})_{\overline{n}}\text{H} + 2n\text{H}_2\text{O}$$

This reaction runs well in practice provided there are no problems of solubility. The catalyst is usually a metallic salt which is sufficiently acidic for the purpose. The water must be removed continuously, and care must be exercised in temperature control so that no cracking of the ester occurs. The biggest practical problem comes in the removal of water from the viscous polymer mass.

The catalyst must not be sufficiently active to cause ether formation from glycol units, because this side reaction will destroy the balance of reacting groups. It will also have the effect of introducing a new monomer unit in the chain and hence some random irregularity, which means a lower melting product with properties different from those of a true glycol polymer.

2. Ester Interchange

$$n\text{HOROH} + n\text{R''}\!-\!\underset{\overset{\|}{O}}{\text{OC}}\!-\!\text{R'}\!-\!\underset{\overset{\|}{O}}{\text{C}}\!-\!\text{OR''} \xrightarrow{\text{cat.}} \text{R''}\!-\!\text{O}\!\left(\underset{\overset{\|}{O}}{\text{C}}\!-\!\text{R'}\!-\!\text{COOR}\!-\!\text{O}\right)_{\!n}\!\!\text{H} +$$

$$2n\text{R'' OH}$$

This procedure often works well. Insoluble acids such as terephthalic acid often give a soluble methyl ester which can be used in such an ester exchange. The catalyst is usually a basic salt. Sodium, aluminum, magnesium, and lithium alkoxides are among the materials used. Because the alcohol to be removed should be as low boiling as possible, methyl esters usually are selected. This method is widely employed for polyethylene terephthalate.

In the reaction involving esterification and ester exchange, the balance between the reagents is very important. In practice, the glycol is frequently used in excess at the beginning and is then removed by distillation to achieve the balance which enables one to form high molecular weight polymers.

3. Anhydride and Glycol

This method is especially valuable for phthalic esters, called alkyds, which are used as surface coatings. They usually involve more complex intermediates and will be considered in detail later.

4. Acid Chloride and Glycol

$$n\text{HOROH} + n\text{ClCOR' COCl} \longrightarrow \text{H}\left[\text{OR}-\text{OCR'}-\overset{\displaystyle O}{\underset{\displaystyle O}{\text{C}}}\right]\text{Cl} + 2n\text{HCl}$$

This method has certain definite limitations. With many glycols a side reaction occurs to replace the OH by halogen. This destroys one hydroxyl of the glycol and is a polymer-ending reaction. Hence only low molecular weight products are formed. This is not invariably true: use of basic acceptors for the hydrogen chloride improves the reaction. Flory and Leutner have found that decamethylene glycol and terephthaloyl chloride will yield a polyester with a molecular weight of over 35,000 by this reaction.[10] Diphenols can be converted to polyesters by this method.

5. Salt of an Acid and a Dihalide

Theoretically this is a satisfactory method of making a polyester, but no case seems to be on record. The salt (NaX) formed would be very difficult to remove from the polymer. The reaction is not a rapid one in many cases, and the yields are not high.

The above are the common reactions for ester formations and are the reactions used for polyesterification. There are others which can undoubtedly be used in special cases, but the first three reactions are the practical methods in use today.

Important Polyester Types

Some practical polyesters of industry are represented by those used for laminating glass fibers. These polyesters contain an unsaturated acid (usually maleic acid) residue which is later involved in a vinyl polymerization reaction. Hence these laminating resins will be considered later after vinyl polymerization has been discussed.

Similar polyesters have been used to produce rubbery materials. The process involves a free radical vulcanization step in the working up of the polyester to convert it to a rubber. Presumably this in-

[10] P. J. Flory and F. S. Leutner, U.S. Patents 2,589,687 and 2,589,688 (1952).

volves attack by the free radical initiator used on an α-hydrogen in the acid with subsequent dimerization to give a crosslink.

$$2H\left(O-R-OC-CH_2-RCH_2C\overset{\overset{O}{\diagup}}{}\right)_n OH \;+\; 2R\cdot \;\longrightarrow$$

$$2H\left(OR-O-\overset{\overset{O}{\parallel}}{C}-\underset{\cdot}{CH}-RCH_2C\overset{\overset{O}{\diagup}}{}\right)_n OH \;+\; 2RH$$

$$H\left(O-R-O\overset{\overset{O}{\parallel}}{C}-CH-RCH_2CO\right)_n OH$$

$$H\left(O-R-O\overset{\overset{O}{\parallel}}{C}-CH-RCH_2CO\right)_n OH$$

The "glyptal" or alkyd resins represent one of the very big fields for polyester use. Originally the "glyptals" were glycerol-phthalic anhydride resins. Since glycerol is trifunctional and phthalic anhydride difunctional, these two reagents give a highly crosslinked material if used alone and if the reaction is pushed to completion.

$$HOCH_2\underset{\underset{OH}{|}}{CH}-\underset{\underset{OH}{|}}{CH_2} \;+\; \left[\text{benzene}\right]\overset{-CO}{\underset{-CO}{\diagdown}}O \;\rightarrow$$

$$\overset{O}{\underset{\diagdown}{C}}O-CH_2-\overset{O}{\underset{|}{CH}}-CH_2-O-$$

In order to get a tractable product the reaction is modified by the use of a glycol along with the glycerol or with some added monobasic acid to replace part of the phthalic acid. By a proper balance of the reactive groups, flexible materials with the correct degree of hardness and solubility can be obtained for use as excellent surface coatings. The current refrigerator enamels incorporate this type of resin.

By introducing long chain glycols, long chain aliphatic dibasic acids, or long chain monobasic acids, further modification of the flexibility can be obtained.

It is perhaps worth noting that the finished alkyd resin which makes a good surface finish has a structure which resembles the material formed by the oxidation (drying) of a drying oil. Drying oils are the glyceryl esters of long chain unsaturated acids. In the drying operation the alkyl chains become crosslinked to give polymeric chains, and the resulting arrangement is more or less that of an alkyd resin structure. This may be represented schematically by

$$
\begin{array}{c}
\mathrm{-CH{=}CH{-}CH_2CH{-}CH(CH_2)_x CH_2{-}C\!\!\stackrel{O}{\overset{\parallel}{{}}}\!\!{-}O{-}CH_2} \\
| \qquad\qquad\qquad\qquad\qquad\qquad\qquad | \\
\mathrm{-CH{=}CH{-}CH_2CH{-}CH(CH_2)_x CH_2{-}C\!\!\stackrel{O}{\overset{\parallel}{{}}}\!\!{-}O{-}CH} \\
| \qquad\qquad\qquad\qquad\qquad\qquad\qquad | \\
\mathrm{-CH{=}CH{-}CH_2CH{-}CH(CH_2)_x CH_2{-}C\!\!\stackrel{O}{\overset{\parallel}{{}}}\!\!{-}O{-}CH_2} \\
|
\end{array}
$$

Polyethylene terephthalate is representative of the linear highly crystalline polyesters which have achieved importance as synthetic fibers (Terylene, Dacron) and synthetic film-forming materials (Mylar). Most polyesters, unless highly crosslinked to produce insolubility, are readily hydrolyzed. But the highly crystalline polyethylene terephthalate is also extremely insoluble and does not hydrolyze readily. It makes an excellent fiber-forming or film-forming polymer. "Cold drawing" (stretching to several times its original length) of the material is necessary to give proper orientation for crystallization and high tensile strength.

Polyester formation and also hydrolysis are affected by the same factors which influence ordinary esterification and hydrolysis. If either the alcohol portion or the acid portion is sterically hindered, these reactions are very slow. Tertiary alcohols undergo dehydration more readily than esterification. Secondary alcohols are intermediate between primary and tertiary.

Simple hydroxy acids are useful for producing polyesters if the spacing of groups is right. They also do not require careful balance of reagents, for the balance occurs in the molecule. α-Hydroxy acids react to give lactides, β-hydroxy acids give α,β- and β,γ-unsaturated acids, γ- and δ-hydroxy acids yield lactones. The higher members of the series give polymers. While the reaction is a good one, it is as yet not of industrial importance because none of the higher hydroxy acids is cheap. Some of the lactones can be caused to open up to give linear polyesters, and some polyesters can be cracked to give cyclic esters. The first type of polymerization is discussed later under "Cyclic Monomers" and "Polyesters."

Polyamides

The ordinary amide-forming reactions which yield monomeric amides (RCONHR) include

1. Reaction of an acid chloride or anhydride with an amine.
2. Heating an ammonium salt.
3. Condensation of ester and amine.

Other reactions can be used to obtain an amide of the type $RC\overset{O}{\overset{\|}{-}}NH_2$, but they are not applicable to polyamide formation.

Polyamides have long attracted the chemist's curiosity because proteins are polyamides of α-amino acids. There are some 22 to 26 naturally occurring α-amino acids which in various combinations build up all the many natural proteins. The synthesis of a protein molecule has long challenged chemists, and Emil Fischer made great progress by preparing an 18-unit polypeptide by a step-wise reaction. This, however, was far from reaching the molecular weight of a protein. The laboratory process of polycondensation cannot be expected to yield an ordered polymer such as a natural protein.

The principal commercial method of forming polyamides is probably the action of heat on the ammonium salt; this has not been used frequently in the amino acid series because the common α-, γ-, and δ-amino acids undergo special self-condensation reactions which prevent polymer formation. Thus an α-amino acid tends to give a diketopiperazine when heated. There are many reports in the lit-

$$^+NH_3-\overset{\overset{\displaystyle R}{\displaystyle |}}{CH}-CO_2^- \longrightarrow$$

erature of polymer formation by the self-condensation of α-amino acid esters. β-Amino acids lose ammonia to give olefinic acids.

Curtius [11] reported the conversion of methyl glycinate to a tetramer and octamer by action of moisture on the ester. Some diketopipera-

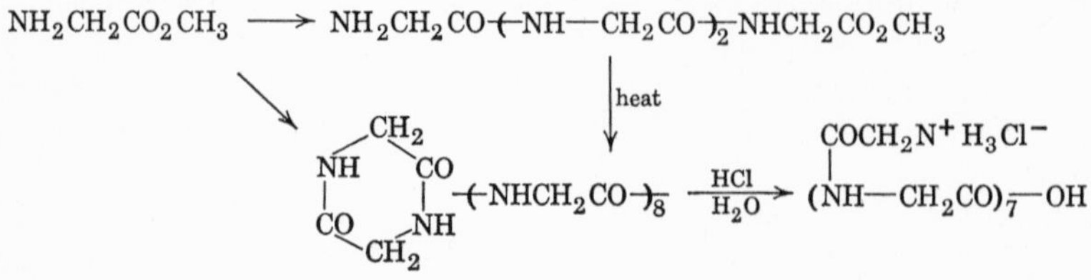

$$NH_2CH_2CO_2CH_3 \longrightarrow NH_2CH_2CO(-NH-CH_2CO)_2^-NHCH_2CO_2CH_3$$

zine is formed in the first step. Curtius believed that the octamer was cyclic and that it could be hydrolyzed with hydrogen chloride to the open chain structure.

Pacsu [12] reported the self-condensation of methyl glycinate to give the polymer shown below in which the integer n equals 12, 24, 48, and 96 according to his estimate.

$$NH_2-CH_2COOCH_3 \longrightarrow H(-NHCH_2CO)_6^- OCH_3 \xrightarrow{heat} H(-NHCH_2CO)_n^- OCH_3$$

These polymers are extremely high melting and insoluble, and their characterization leaves something to be desired.

More recently the Leuchs reaction [13] of carboanhydrides to give linear polymers has again been receiving renewed study, and interesting polyamides have been prepared from α-amino acids. This reac-

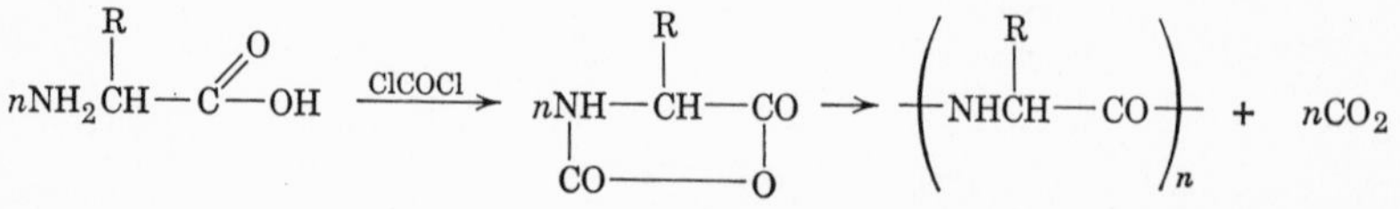

tion is not one ordinarily used for amide formation and is probably more nearly like vinyl polymerization in its mechanism. Polymers prepared by this procedure have molecular weights of 15,000 to 25,000 and, depending on the R group, may be soluble and hence are capable of fabrication into films and fibers of considerable interest. The reaction is undoubtedly initiated by water with H and OH becoming the end groups in the final polymer.

β-Amino acids lose ammonia when heated and hence are not useful

---

[11] T. Curtius, *Ber.*, **37**, 1284 (1904).

[12] E. Pacsu, *Nature*, **144**, 551 (1939).

[13] H. Leuchs, *Ber.*, **39**, 857 (1906).

in forming stable high polymers. γ- and δ-Amino acids give cyclic lactams. Amino acids with greater spacing between the $-NH_2$ and $-CO_2H$ groups furnish linear polymers. The most interesting of these polymers is probably the polymer of ϵ-aminocaproic acid which is currently coming on the American market as a nylon fiber. The route to the polymer is

This is a case of converting a cyclic lactam to a linear polyamide. It may be catalyzed by sodium or by a trace of moisture. Other initiators also are known. The final end groups are probably $-H$ and $-OH$. The polymer can be produced by heating ϵ-aminocaproic acid, but that procedure is not now practical. The polymerization of the lactam is not strictly a condensation reaction from the mechanism standpoint. These cyclic monomers will be mentioned later, but the current importance of this polyamide makes its inclusion here important.

By far the most important practical polyamides are those produced from diamines and dibasic acids by the action of heat on their salts, leading to polymers with a molecular weight in the 20,000 range. Polyhexamethyleneadipamide is the best-known nylon and because of its technical importance has received the most study. It is prepared by heating the hexamethylenediamine salt of adipic acid above the melting point in a nitrogen atmosphere. The last condition is important to prevent discoloration due to oxidation. The salt is prepared and recrystallized to be sure that there is a strict balance of carboxyl and amine end groups. If a specific end group is desired, a calculated excess of amine or acid may be used. Or the polymer may be viscosity stabilized by adding to the reaction mixture either a monofunctional amine or acid.

Polyamides have been prepared by the action of a diacid chloride on a diamine,

$$n\text{ClCORCOCl} + n\text{NH}_2\text{R}'\text{NH}_2 \rightarrow \text{Cl}(\text{CORCONHR}'\text{NH})_n\text{H} + 2n\text{HCl}$$

and by condensation of an ester of a dibasic acid and a diamine,

$$n\text{CH}_3\text{OCORCOOCH}_3 + n\text{NH}_2\text{R}'\text{NH}_2 \rightarrow$$

$$\text{CH}_3\text{O}(\text{CORCONHR}'\text{NH})_n\text{H} + 2n\text{CH}_3\text{OH}$$

In place of alkyl esters, phenyl esters are useful in this type of reaction for preparing polyamides. These esters are quite reactive, and the phenol does not have to be distilled from the reaction mixture. It dissolves in the polymer and can be washed out later in the process. However, these methods do not seem to have much technical importance.

Polyamides can be made from disecondary amines, RNHR'NHR, but the amidation is much slower and it is more difficult to obtain high molecular weight materials.

Polyamides are generally products with fairly high melting points and rather low solubilities. They can be dissolved in hot formic acid, some phenols, and a few complexing agents, but they are generally insoluble in common solvents. If the units are symmetrical and unbranched (no asymmetric carbon atoms), they show considerable crystallinity when cold drawn. If branched chain monomers such as β-methyladipic acid or β-methylhexamethylenediamine are used, the polyamides are lower melting and more soluble. The introduction of cyclic monomer units into the chain usually greatly increases the intractability (high melting point, low solubility) of a polyamide.

Cold drawing of polyamides is usually necessary to convert them into strong, tough fibers or films. In practice, nylon is prepared in a melt and spun into fibers from the melt. These fibers are then stretched to as much as 400 to 500% of their original length. This drawing or stretching seems to line up the linear polymers into an oriented state, which is evidenced by the change in x-ray pattern, a strong birefringence with parallel extinction, and other unusual properties not shown by undrawn material. Also, there is a marked increase in elasticity and toughness. This seems to be in part due to the hydrogen bonding between amide chains.

When polyamides are prepared from substituted amines with fairly long R groups and irregularity is introduced by using mixed amines or mixtures of mono- and disubstituted amines (R'NHRNHR and R'NHRNH$_2$), rubbery polyamides can be produced. These have been produced commercially but have never been large volume products.

Polyamides can be hydrolyzed. They undergo slow oxidation in air, and this is one of the causes of yellowing of nylon on exposure to sunlight.

In addition to use as a fiber, polyamides are used for bristles and for molded products. Their toughness makes them especially valuable for gears which have to withstand service for long periods.

Reactions at an Interface

In 1955 a patent was issued to Magat and Strachan [14] covering the formation of superpolymer films and filaments by a liquid phase polymerization of fast reacting intermediates. This is accomplished by conducting an interphase reaction between fast reacting groups at the surface between two liquid phases.

For example, a 10% by weight solution of adipyl chloride in chlorobenzene is fed slowly into a 2% by weight solution of hexamethylenediamine in water at 25° at the rate of about 0.1 gram of solution per minute through a fine orifice. The polymer which forms as the two solutions come in contact is drawn off and wound up continuously. When the diamine and diacid chloride are mixed in a common solvent, only low molecular weight polymer is produced. This reaction at an interface yields a product of good strength with an inherent viscosity of 1.26, which indicates a high molecular weight.

A symposium on interfacial polycondensations was presented at the Chicago meeting of the American Chemical Society in September 1958.[15] The especial advantages of this type of polycondensation are that heat sensitive polymers can be obtained, and also polymers which otherwise could not be handled because of infusibility or insolubility can be obtained in fiber or film form for examination. The method has been used to prepare polyurethans, polyamides, polyureas, polysulfonamides, and polyphenyl esters. It has been shown that the two phase system may be allowed to stand and the polymer which forms at the interfacial surface can be drawn off as a film or collapsed tube to give a dramatic demonstration experiment. Sometimes it is better to stir the two phase system and produce polymer at the interface between the particles. Some polyamides with sensitive groups such as hydroxyl or carbon-carbon unsaturation have been synthesized readily by this technique. Very high molecular weight

[14] E. E. Magat and D. R. Strachan, U.S. Patent 2,708,617 (1955).

[15] The speakers at this symposium were all members of the staff of the Pioneering Research Division, Textile Fibers Department, E. I. du Pont de Nemours and Company, Wilmington, Delaware. Papers were presented by E. L. Wittbecker and P. W. Morgan; R. G. Beaman, C. R. Koller, E. E. Magat, P. W. Morgan, and E. L. Wittbecker; M. Katz; S. A. Sundet, W. A. Murphey and S. B. Speck; E. L. Wittbecker and M. Katz; J. R. Schaefgen, F. H. Koontz, and R. F. Tietz; W. M. Eareckson III; and P. W. Morgan and S. L. Kwolek at the Symposium on Condensation Polymers, Division of Polymer Chemistry, American Chemical Society Meeting, Chicago, Illinois, September 8, 1958.

polyurethans have been obtained from ethylenediamine, aromatic diamines, and cyclic secondary amines by condensing them in interfacial systems with the bis-chloroformate of glycols or diphenols.

The method can be used for a self-condensation of such a molecule as $NH_2(CH_2)_5COCl$ by blocking the amine group as a hydrochloride and then liberating the base slowly by adding an inorganic base. But this type of polycondensation is not as good as the reaction of two molecules such as a diamine and a diacid chloride.

Phenol-Aldehyde Resins

The first important industrial synthetic polymer was Bakelite, the phenol-formaldehyde heat hardening resin. The type of condensation reaction involved in its formation was studied by Baeyer[16] over 80 years ago. He was followed by other chemists, but Baekeland really developed the practical side of the resin-forming reaction and received patents covering useful preparations in the early 1900's. Since then many scientific workers have contributed to our knowledge of these resins.

The reaction of phenol with formaldehyde is promoted by either acid or alkaline catalysts. It is generally believed to proceed through aldol type addition of phenol in the o- and p-positions to the carbonyl group of formaldehyde to yield hydroxybenzyl alcohols which in turn condense in o- and p-positions to give diphenylmethane links. Since there are three active positions in phenol and two active positions in formaldehyde, we have the same 3–2 functionality exhibited by glycerol-phthalic anhydride mixtures, and crosslinked polymers are produced.

16 A. Baeyer, *Ber.*, **5,** 280, 1094 (1878).

In basic catalyzed condensations the phenolic hydroxyl is certainly not involved in the condensation, since the first low molecular weight polymers produced are alkali soluble. If *o*- or *p*-monosubstituted phenols are used, the crosslinking possibilities disappear and low molecular weight soluble polymers can be produced. Some monosubstituted (*o* or *p*) phenol may be mixed with the phenol in the reaction above to give modified resins with less crosslinking in much the same manner that modified glyptals are prepared by replacing some of the dibasic acid constituent by a monobasic acid in the reaction mixture used for the formation of those polymers. The phenol-formaldehyde reaction is carried out in bulk until a powdery polymer is obtained. For curing, this powder is compressed in a mold and heated to set up the resin to the crosslinked insoluble infusible stage.

When acid catalysts are used for the phenol-aldehyde reaction, the course of the condensation is changed because even the low molecular weight resins are alkali insoluble. It has been suggested that acetal formation occurs and that even ether formation may be involved. The increase in functionality caused by reaction of the hydroxyl group makes crosslinking even more complex.

Aldehydes other than formaldehyde have been used in this condensation. Instead of phenols, aromatic amines have been used to produce the Ciba resins. In these resins anil formation between the amine group and the aldehyde and also the ring condensations are involved in the polymer formation. There is no good information available on the probable molecular size of phenol-aldehyde resins, but they probably are not high molecular weight until after the final thermosetting reaction in the molds.

Urea-Formaldehyde Resins

Urea and formaldehyde condense under alkaline or acid conditions to give methylol- and dimethylolureas which can be isolated as crystalline materials. The reaction is reversible, and formaldehyde can be lost from a methylol- or dimethylolurea to regenerate the $-NH_2$ group.

$$NH_2CONH_2 \rightleftharpoons NH_2CONHCH_2OH \rightleftharpoons HOCH_2NHCONHCH_2OH$$

Further heating of these intermediates with formaldehyde leads to the formation of polymeric powders which are soon insoluble and infusible. In practice, relatively low molecular weight polymer is produced and heated in a mold under pressure to produce the commercial articles which are known so well.

There has been a great deal of speculation on the manner by which this polymerization reaction occurs. Probably no one mechanism or single structural formula for the recurring unit of the polymer can be written for this case. If we consider what is known of amide reactions with formaldehyde, we can suggest some of the better possibilities for polymer structure. The earliest suggestion for the course of the polymer-

ization was that the methylol intermediate dehydrated to a $-N\!\!=\!\!\overset{|}{C}-$ type, and this was supposed to polymerize by a vinyl type polymerization.

$$
\begin{array}{cccc}
\text{NH—CH}_2\text{OH} & \text{N}\!\!=\!\!\text{CH}_2 & \text{NHCH}_2\text{OH} & \text{N}\!\!=\!\!\text{CH}_2 \\
| & | & | & | \\
\text{CO} \quad \rightarrow & \text{CO} & \text{CO} \quad \rightarrow & \text{CO} \\
| & | & | & | \\
\text{NH}_2 & \text{NH}_2 & \text{NHCH}_2\text{OH} & \text{N}\!\!=\!\!\text{CH}_2
\end{array}
$$

However, we have no similar examples of $-N\!\!=\!\!\overset{|}{C}-$ polymerizations to support this view, and it is now seldom seriously considered as the mechanism of polymer formation. When a simple amide is heated with formaldehyde, it can be converted to a methylol derivative or to a bis-methylene amide type.

$$
\overset{\text{O}}{\underset{}{\text{RC}\!\!\parallel}}\!\!-\!\!\text{NH}_2 \rightarrow \overset{\text{O}}{\underset{}{\text{RC}\!\!\parallel}}\!\!-\!\!\text{NHCH}_2\text{OH} \rightarrow \overset{\text{O}}{\underset{}{\text{RC}\!\!\parallel}}\!\!-\!\!\text{NHCH}_2\text{NHCOR}
$$

The bis-methylene amide can further be converted to a methylol deriva-tive.

$$
\overset{\text{O}}{\underset{}{\text{RC}\!\!\parallel}}\!\!-\!\!\underset{|}{\text{N}}\!\!-\!\!\text{CH}_2\text{NHCOR}
$$
$$
\text{CH}_2\text{OH}
$$

If both NH_2 groups in urea can undergo such a condensation, it would be reasonable to suppose that a linear polymerization occurs with some secondary crosslinking, for example,

$$
\begin{array}{l}
\text{--CH}_2\text{NHCONCH}_2\text{NHCONHCH}_2\text{N(H)CONH—} \\
\qquad | \qquad\qquad\qquad\qquad | \\
\qquad \text{CH}_2\text{(OH)} \qquad\quad \text{CH}_2\text{(OH)} \\
\text{—CH}_2\text{NHCON(H)—CH}_2\text{NHCONHCH}_2\text{N—CONH—}
\end{array}
$$

Many variations can be devised. But the mechanism is not entirely satisfactory because it would predict that monosubstituted and symmetrically disubstituted ureas should give polymers with formaldehyde, and no such polymers have been prepared.

Other intermediates which are known to form from urea and formaldehyde are cyclic derivatives such as

$$\begin{array}{ccc} & CO\!-\!NH & \\ NH & & CH_2 \\ & CH_2\!-\!N & \\ & | & \\ & CONH_2 & \end{array} \qquad \begin{array}{ccc} & NH\!-\!CH_2 & \\ CO & & O \\ & NH\!-\!CH_2 & \end{array}$$

These have been suggested as units which are further condensed and crosslinked by additional formaldehyde reactions on the $>$NH and NH$_2$ sites. These structures would require fairly definite ratios of formaldehyde to urea, actually somewhat higher than need be used in practice.

Another suggestion which has received some favor is based on the idea that urea is both an amide and an amine. In keeping with this idea, it is reasonable to assume the basic NH$_2$ might form a Schiff's base with formaldehyde which would trimerize readily as do most simple Schiff's bases.

$$3\ \begin{array}{c} N\!=\!CH_2 \\ | \\ CO \\ | \\ NH_2 \end{array} \quad \rightarrow \quad \begin{array}{c} CONH_2 \\ | \\ N \\ CH_2 \quad CH_2 \\ NH_2CO\!-\!N \qquad N\!-\!CONH_2 \\ CH_2 \end{array}$$

This cyclic structure has three primary amide groups which could form bis-methylene amide structures with more formaldehyde, and

$$\begin{array}{c} NHCH_2\!- \\ | \\ CO \\ | \\ N \\ CH_2 \qquad CH_2 \\ -CH_2\!-\!NHCON \qquad N\!-\!CONHCH_2\!- \\ CH_2 \end{array}$$

this would provide the 3–2 functionality which has been observed in glyptal or phenol-formaldehyde polymers and which give highly cross-linked structures. The ratio of urea to formaldehyde needed for this condensation reaction agrees very closely with that used by the best-known urea-formaldehyde resin manufacturers. It seems doubtful, however, whether this unit is the only one produced, and many of the other possible units and further methylol condensation products from these structures are probably involved.

It should be explained that low molecular weight water soluble materials can be made in these condensations. The soluble products become insoluble on heating, and finally the resins are crosslinked by molding to give durable molded products of excellent color. When the water soluble resins are used for treating textiles, they are "set up" to insoluble polymers by ironing the cloth. Another innovation is the introduction of alcohols into the reaction mixtures which can lead to oil soluble low molecular weight urea-formaldehyde condensation products. It is possible to isolate such intermediates as

$$
\begin{array}{ccc}
\mathrm{NHCH_2OR} & \qquad & \mathrm{NHCH_2OR} \\
| & & | \\
\mathrm{CO} & & \mathrm{CO} \\
| & & | \\
\mathrm{NH_2} & & \mathrm{NHCH_2OR}
\end{array}
$$

These methylol ethers can be condensed much as the methylolureas themselves. If R is of high molecular weight, oil solubility is induced until crosslinking becomes too great.

A close relative of the urea-formaldehyde type resin is the melamine type produced from melamine and formaldehyde. Melamine is

$$
\mathrm{NH_2CN} \rightarrow
$$

Melamine

trimeric cyanamide. The formaldehyde condensation is believed to give Schiff's base structures which in turn trimerize to give the complex cyclic derivatives. The low molecular weight methylol-rich intermediates are soluble enough to use for textile applications, which have become very important.

Thiokols (Polyalkylene Polysulfides)

Ethylene chloride and sodium polysulfide react on heating together to produce a polymeric polysulfide. The nature of the end groups

$$x\,ClCH_2CH_2Cl + x\,Na_2S_4 \longrightarrow -(CH_2CH_2-S_4)_x + 2x\,NaCl$$

depends on which reagent is in excess. If excess ethylene chloride is used, a low molecular weight viscous liquid results. If sodium polysulfide is in excess, a tough rubbery product is formed. It seems probable that this course of the reaction leads to polymers with —SH end groups which tend to oxidize to give more —S—S— groups and hence higher molecular weight materials.

The rubbery polymers can be vulcanized by heating with zinc oxide and water with further increase in the molecular size.

The condensation polymers obtained by the above reaction can be desulfurized to a polymeric ethylene disulfide which can be reduced to ethylene dimercaptan. The reverse operation can also be accomplished. Other fairly active halogen compounds have been used to give rub-

$$n\,HS-CH_2CH_2SH \underset{red}{\overset{ox}{\rightleftharpoons}} -(CH_2CH_2-S-S)_n \underset{-S}{\overset{+S}{\rightleftharpoons}} \left(CH_2CH_2-\underset{S}{\overset{S}{\underset{|}{\overset{|}{S}}}}-\underset{S}{\overset{S}{\underset{|}{\overset{|}{S}}}}\right)_n$$

bery polysulfides. Dichlorodiethyl ether, $ClCH_2CH_2OCH_2CH_2Cl$, the formal of ethylene chlorohydrin, $ClCH_2CH_2O-CH_2-O-CH_2CH_2Cl$, and trimethylene chloride are reagents which have been commonly used. The thiokols have been used as flight deck caulking agents in the decks of airplane carriers in the Navy. More recently the thiokol type of polymer has been used as a component of solid rocket fuels.

Polyurethans

The reaction of a diisocyanate with a glycol leads to a polyurethan, and a variety of polymers of this type has been prepared.

$$O=C=NR-N=C=O + HOR'OH \rightarrow$$

$$\overset{H\quad O}{\underset{|\quad\;\|}{O=C=N-R-N-C-OR'-OH}} \quad \ldots\ldots \text{polymer}$$

One of the first to achieve practical importance was the polymer prepared from hexamethylene diisocyanate and tetramethylene glycol. This polymer makes excellent bristles which have been used industrially by the Germans.

The isocyanates are made from diamines and phosgene. The reaction is successful with either aliphatic or aromatic amines and for mono-, di-, and triamines. Isocyanates are sensitive to moisture and react with alcohols, acids, and amines so that side reactions with impurities must be considered carefully.

During the war years, the I. G. Farbenindustrie Akt.-Ges. found that the complex polyurethans had many interesting properties as adhesives, particularly to bond resins to metal surfaces and to make rubbery materials called Vullcolans.

The adhesives for bonding metals are usually made from alkyd resins and a diisocyanate such as hexamethylene diisocyanate (Desmodur H). The polyester with terminal —OH groups is crosslinked by the isocyanate, and also the isocyanate seems to bond onto the metal surface in a surprising manner, perhaps through surface water or oxide.

Drying oils are also improved by making some modifications through isocyanate reactions. If a triglyceride is converted to a diglyceride and then treated with a chlorinated phenylene diisocyanate, new gloss, hardness, and less swelling by water are said to be introduced into the surface coating produced.

One of the most exciting new uses for the urethan plastics is in making either flexible or rigid foams by treating a polyester with a diisocyanate under conditions which crosslink the polyester. This reaction produces much carbon dioxide to foam the reaction mass. The crosslinking occurs by the usual glycol-isocyanate reaction. Foaming (CO_2 production) may come from the reaction of moisture or carboxyl end groups with the isocyanate groups.

$$2R—N{=}C{=}O + H_2O \rightarrow RNHCONHR + CO_2$$

$$R'—\overset{\displaystyle O}{\overset{\|}{C}}—OH + RN{=}C{=}O \rightarrow R'—\overset{\displaystyle O}{\overset{\|}{C}}—NHR' + CO_2$$

If diisocyanates are used, urea recurring units are introduced into the polymers by these two reactions.

To obtain a flexible foam which will weigh 2 to 6 pounds per cubic foot, a mixture of 15 to 40 parts of diisocyanate and 100 parts of polyester is used. To obtain a rigid plastic foam for insulation purposes which may weigh from 6 to 30 pounds per cubic foot, 60 to 100 parts of diisocyanate are treated with 100 parts of polyester.

Currently the urethans seem to be most used in surface coatings or foams.

The Germans developed Vullcolan rubbers, which were polyesters crosslinked with isocyanates. These have extremely good abrasive properties but never have found commercial use because they are expensive and do not seem to withstand other conditions imposed on a rubber.[17-24]

Epoxy Resins

Epoxy resins are defined as resinous substances or resin-forming compounds which contain the epoxide group and/or a derivative thereof which may be formed by causing the substances to undergo reactions with another reagent such as water, ammonia, an amine, an alcohol, a phenol, or an acid or acid anhydride.

These resins have been developed by the Shell group (Epons) and the Devoe Raynolds group. Greenlee seems to hold the basic patent.[25]

The common synthesis involves the condensation of epichlorohydrin with a diphenolic compound followed eventually by a crosslinking reaction with an amine. A typical example is

The crosslinking reaction involves the opening up of the terminal oxide links with amines such as diethylenetriamine to give the final resin. This triamine may react in a variety of ways with the epoxide,

[17] G. M. Kline, *Modern Plastics*, **23**, 152 (1945).

[18] R. S. Krausen, *Silk J.*, **21**, 28, 36 (1946).

[19] H. Rinke and P. Weikart, German Patent 728,002 (1942).

[20] P. Schlack, U.S. Patent 2,343,808 (1944).

[21] H. Vittenet, *Bull. soc. chim.*, (3) **21**, 952 (1899).

[22] British Patent 535,139 (1941).

[23] J. H. Saunders and R. J. Slocombe, *Chem. Revs.*, **43**, 203 (1948).

[24] H. L. Heiss, J. H. Saunders, M. R. Morris, B. R. Davis, and E. E. Hardy, *Ind. Eng. Chem.*, **46**, 1498 (1954).

[25] S. O. Greenlee, U.S. Patents 2,456,408 (1948) and 2,493,486 (1950).

but if the simplest manner is considered we have two reactive epoxides and three reactive hydrogens on nitrogen which give the 3–2 functionality that leads to crosslinking.

$$-CH_2-\overset{\displaystyle O}{\overset{\displaystyle /\ \ \backslash}{CH}}-CH_2 + NH_2CH_2CH_2NHCH_2CH_2NH_2 \rightarrow$$

$$-CH_2-\overset{\displaystyle OH}{\overset{|}{CH}}-CH_2NHCH_2CH_2NHCH_2CH_2NH_2 \rightarrow \text{ etc.}$$

The first condensation product of the epichlorohydrin and the diphenol varies in molecular weight depending on the end use to which it is to be put. The variation seems to be in the range of 890 to 2900 molecular weight in the common resins.

Three major uses of epoxy resins have been suggested. When reacted with heat convertible resins such as phenol-formaldehyde and urea-formaldehyde resins, they produce films of very high outdoor performance. When treated with amines they give a cured film with a high order of chemical resistance which is produced at room temperatures. The most widely used modification seems to be that of esterification with fatty or rosin acids under the influence of heat to yield products useful in floor finishes, primer coatings, can liners, and the like.

Epoxy resins are noted for adhesion, flexibility, toughness, and chemical resistance. It is thought these features are due to crosslinking at suitable distances along the chain to give some of the flexibility effects of the long sections between crosslinks. Their compatibility with a wide variety of other film-forming products increases their range of usefulness.

In addition to their extensive use in surface coatings epoxy resins can be used for potting resins. These are resins that can be poured into molds at room temperature and then allowed to set up to tough crosslinked materials which have good stability, hold their dimensions well under strain, and stand shock and very rough handling extremely well.

It is, of course, possible to use phenols other than the diphenylol propane suggested. Epoxides other than epichlorohydrin might be used, but none has become cheap enough to be significant in the market.

Silicone Resins

The name silicone came into use because these resins were once thought to be silicon analogs of ketones. However, they are polymeric materials and not simple molecules with a silicon-oxygen double bond.

When silicon tetrachloride is hydrolyzed, polymeric silicon dioxide, SiO_2, with various degrees of hydration results and eventually dries down to the dehydrated form. When one or two of the chlorine atoms of silicon tetrachloride are replaced by alkyl or aryl groups, the hydrolysis again gives polymers which are linear in the case of R_2SiCl_2 and crosslinked in the case of $RSiCl_3$. R_3SiCl yields a siloxane, $R_3SiOSiR_3$.

In practical work the polymeric materials of interest are mainly the products of hydrolysis of disubstituted silicon dichlorides which give linear polymeric oils and rubbery polymers. If a small amount of $RSiCl_3$ is hydrolyzed along with the R_2SiCl_2, a degree of crosslinking results and this can be used as a means of "vulcanizing" a rubbery polymer.

There are two characteristic properties of these silicones which render them of great value. One is their marked flexibility at low temperature, and the other is their stability at relatively high temperatures. The first of these two properties has been ascribed to the Si—O—Si bond which is uncrowded and has plenty of room for rotation. Facetiously, it has been termed a universal joint in the molecule which gives great freedom of movement. Actually the silicone oils do not freeze to solids at dry ice and even liquid air temperatures. Rather they flow almost as freely at $-100°$ as they do at $0°$. This makes these polymeric oils of importance in hydraulic components of airplane parts. An ordinary brake oil will congeal at temperatures encountered at high altitudes and then fail to function properly when a plane descends suddenly. The relatively constant viscosity over an extremely wide temperature range is a characteristic of the silicone group.

The silicon polymers which are solid or rubbery or both are used for high temperature insulation and in places where rubbery materials must be useful at elevated temperatures. These silicones are good up to about $250°$. When heated much higher they begin to depolymerize by cleaving cyclic units from the chain. These cyclic units are usually six- and eight-membered rings of silicon-oxygen atoms but may be even larger sized rings.

The practical silicones are those which have methyl and phenyl groups attached to the silicon. These intermediates are produced by Grignard reactions or sometimes by direct action of the alkyl halide with silicon.

$$2RMgX + SiCl_4 \rightarrow R_2SiCl_2 + MgX_2 + MgCl_2$$

$$2RX + Si \rightarrow R_2SiX_2$$

Side reactions accompany the last reaction, yielding such products as

$$3RX + Si \rightarrow R\dot{S}iX_3 + (2R)$$

$$3RX + Si \rightarrow R_3SiX + X_2$$

$$2X_2 + Si \rightarrow SiX_4, \quad \text{etc.}$$

Sometimes the degradation of R radicals gives enough hydrogen so reduction occurs to yield $RSiHX_2$ types.

The exact details for converting these carbon silicon halides to silicone oils and rubbers can be obtained from patent literature, but the process is essentially a controlled hydrolysis. The first product is probably cyclic, and this is then polymerized to the long chain needed to give the strong rubbers.

$$R_2SiCl_2 + 2H_2O \longrightarrow \left(\begin{array}{c} R \\ | \\ -Si-O- \\ | \\ R \end{array} \right) + 2HCl$$

The terminal groups are hydroxyl unless one uses R_3SiCl as a "capping" agent; then an R_3SiO will be the end group.[26]

Addition Polymerization
(*Free Radical Initiation*)

Vinyl Polymers

Vinyl polymers are produced from olefins by chain polymerization reactions which usually lead to high molecular weight products. In contrast to condensation polymerizations there seem to be no inter-

[26] E. G. Rochow, *An Introduction to the Chemistry of the Silicones,* John Wiley & Sons, Inc., New York, 1946.

mediate low molecular weight units which slowly produce the high molecular weight materials. Not all olefins undergo the reaction, but the number which do increases as chemists learn more about these reactions.

1. Polymerizable Types

Ethylene, $CH_2{=}CH_2$, is the only aliphatic hydrocarbon which polymerizes well under free radical conditions. Propylene and isobutylene are unreactive and give only oils under conditions which yield high polymers with ethylene. 1,2-Disubstituted ethylenes do not polymerize.

In the halogenated series, vinyl chloride, vinylidene chloride, vinyl bromide, vinyl fluoride, vinylidene fluoride, chlorotrifluoroethylene, and tetrafluoroethylene all polymerize. Trichloro- and tetrachloroethylene polymers have not been prepared.

Vinyl esters of aliphatic acids, $CH_2{=}CHO{-}COR$, are almost always readily polymerized, as are vinyl esters of sulfonic acids, $CH_2{=}CHO{-}SO_2R$.

Acrylic acid and its esters, α-methylacrylic acid and its esters, acrylonitrile, α-methylacrylonitrile, methyl vinyl ketone, and methyl isopropenyl ketone are readily polymerized. Groups larger than $CH_3{-}$ on the α-carbon seem to slow down the polymerization.

Monoarylethylenes such as styrene, , and β-furylethylene, , are readily polymerizable by free radical

initiators. However, substitution of even a methyl group for a hydrogen atom on either side of the double bond slows down these polymerizations markedly. Some substitutions in the aryl ring accelerate the polymerizations of monomers of this type.

A very wide variety of substituted olefins will undergo copolymerization with some of these polymerizable materials but will not polymerize alone. These types will be covered in the section titled "Copolymerization."

2. Mechanism of Free Radical Initiated Polymerization

It is generally believed that this type of polymerization involves three distinct steps called initiation, propagation, and termination.

These steps really apply to all addition types of polymerizations whether free radical or not, but at this point only the cases where free radical initiation is involved in the initiation step will be considered.

We may represent these steps by the following.

(1) $\qquad$ R· + CH$_2$=CHY → RCH$_2$—ĊHY $\qquad$ Initiation

Here a radical attaches itself to the olefin and produces the new radical consisting of the initiator fragment and one unit of monomer.

(2) RCH$_2$CHY· + nCH$_2$=CHY → R(CH$_2$CHY)·$_{n+1}$ Propagation

This step is a very rapid one. No low molecular weight polymers are produced in systems if the reaction conditions are favorable to growth.

(3) Termination may occur by several processes. Coupling is termination by combination of two growing radicals.

$$2R(CH_2\text{—}CHY)\cdot_n \rightarrow R(CH_2CHY)_n\text{:}(CHY\text{—}CH_2)_nR$$

Disproportionation involves termination by transfer of hydrogen to another molecule to terminate it or to start a new chain. It has been suggested that disproportionation gives a hydrogen radical:

R—(CH$_2$CHY)$_n$—CH$_2$—CHY· → R(CH$_2$—CHY)$_n$—CH=CHY + H·

H·

⟶ R(CH$_2$CHY)$_n$—CH$_2$CH$_2$Y

or new chain H—(CH$_2$CHY)·. It is more likely that this is only a special case of chain transfer in which one growing chain abstracts a hydrogen from another growing chain or polymer molecule.

Chain transfer is also a mechanism of termination. It involves the use of a chain transfer agent which is capable of ending one chain and starting another. Such agents have been called telomerizing agents (Greek *telos* means end).

$$R(CH_2\text{—}CHY)\cdot_n + HSR \rightarrow R(CH_2\text{—}CHY)_n\text{:}H + RS\cdot$$

$$RS\cdot + n(CH_2\text{=}CHY) \rightarrow RS(CH_2\text{—}CHY)_n\cdot$$

Chain transfer agents will be considered more fully later.

Special techniques have been devised for measuring the rates of the different steps, and usually the rate-determining step for the over-all polymerization is the initiation step. It is sometimes difficult to decide how the termination step occurs.

By use of radioactive initiators and a study of the number of initiator fragments per polymer molecule, Bevington, Melville, and Taylor[27] have shown that polystyrene chains are terminated primarily by combination and polymethyl methacrylate chains are terminated by both disproportionation (2 parts) and combination (1 part). Chain transfer termination is widely used in practical work and has been well established by analytical means, with both radioactive and regular methods.

3. Polymerization Systems

Polymerization of vinyl compounds by free radical initiation may be accomplished in bulk, solution, suspension, or emulsion systems. There are advantages and disadvantages to each method.

When bulk polymerization is used, the initiator is usually a compound which decomposes to give radicals at a fairly rapid rate at relatively low temperatures. Bulk polymerization is used now mainly to cast objects in a particular shape where molding at elevated temperatures cannot be done, for example, casting of a methyl methacrylate polymer over a flower, insect, or some other fragile object which would be destroyed by heat. When large amounts of monomer are polymerized in bulk, the heat transfer problem becomes serious and hot spots develop in the polymerization mass, causing decomposition and side reactions. Some polyvinyl chloride is made by bulk polymerization; the polymer is not soluble in the monomer and falls out as a powder.

Solution polymerization is often not entirely satisfactory. As the size of the polymer grows, the viscosity of the solution becomes very great. Stirring to facilitate heat transfer becomes difficult. There are methods of polymerization used commercially in which the monomer is put in a solvent and at a certain range of growth the polymer becomes insoluble and falls out as a bead or suspended particle. This process is satisfactory for methyl methacrylate in methanol and for acrylonitrile in water solutions. The initiator used must be soluble in the solvent and produce radicals at the temperature desired. Chain transfer interferes with many attempts at solution polymerization. Few solvents are sufficiently inert to free radical attack.

Emulsion polymerization is a common practical method of operation. The monomer is emulsified in water with an emulsifier that can be acidic, basic, or neutral. The two phase system is particularly use-

[27] J. C. Bevington, H. W. Melville, and R. P. Taylor, *J. Polymer Sci.,* **12,** 449 (1954).

ful in redox (reduction-oxidation) systems, and these will be discussed in detail under "Initiators." The big advantage of emulsion systems is their fluidity, which permits good heat transfer, thus circumventing the problem of local overheating. There is no chain transfer with water. High molecular weight material can be formed and can be transferred in emulsion without viscosity effects interfering. The emulsion system cannot be used with water sensitive monomers.

Almost any type of emulsifier can be used. Soaps and synthetic detergents are both common. Even some of the non-ionic polymeric materials such as polyvinyl alcohol and proteins work well. One problem in using soap was encountered in the synthetic rubber industry. The soaps derived from linoleic and linolenic acids are inhibitors of free radical polymerizations because of the $-CH=CHCH_2CH=$ $CH-$ structure present in the chain. Any trace of a salt of one of these acids can be detected by its effect in slowing polymerization. It became necessary to write soap specifications which excluded such substances from the soap to be used in the polymerization industry.

4. Initiators

A number of polymerizations are initiated by heat and by ultra-violet irradiation. Such polymerizations appear to be initiated by radicals produced by heat or ultraviolet irradiation of the monomer.

Usually the initiator is a peroxide, hydroperoxide, an azonitrile, or some closely related material which can be readily converted to a free radical under the conditions suitable for the desired polymerization.

There is a wide variety of inorganic materials which are good initiators. They may be used in aqueous solution or suspension. Various persulfates, perborates, permanganates, and hydrogen peroxide have been and are being used alone or in combination with activators. Often the salt of a metal of variable valence is needed to convert these initiators into free radicals.

Among the organic reagents, benzoyl peroxide is one that has been

$$\overset{O}{\overset{\|}{}}$$

extensively used. It decomposes to $C_6H_5C\!-\!O\cdot$ and $C_6H_5\cdot + CO_2$ to produce the initiating radicals. It is most active at temperatures of 80° and above. Other organic peroxides have been used. The diaryl peroxides are usually better than such dialkyl peroxides as di-t-butyl peroxide. The latter is too stable to yield radicals rapidly enough for some practical uses.

The development of the so-called redox system has led to a marked increase of the use of hydroperoxides as initiators. Some hydroperoxides decompose rapidly and need no activation. Others require a reducing agent for effective use. Acetyl hydroperoxide or peracetic acid is water soluble and needs to be used with water soluble monomers to give best results.

Currently the aromatic hydroperoxides are the ones receiving greatest attention, especially in emulsion systems such as are used in making synthetic rubber. Oil soluble hydroperoxides such as cumene hydroperoxide and diisopropylbenzene hydroperoxide are used along with a metal of variable valence (Fe^{II}) to give a fast system of polymerization. This reaction results in production of radicals which

$$ROOH + Fe^{++} \rightarrow RO\cdot + OH^- + Fe^{+++}$$

are capable of initiating polymerization. Kolthoff [28] believes the $RO\cdot$ radical degrades further to give a carbon radical.

In an emulsion system the rate of radical generation can be governed by the solubility of the organic hydroperoxide, the complexing agent used for the metal, the water soluble reducing agent used to regenerate reduced metal ions, etc. If the iron and the peroxide are in the oil phase, the radicals are quickly generated but polymerization may die out without complete conversion. If a system is used which generates radicals too slowly, the polymerization does not proceed fast enough. A careful balance of monomer, initiator, activator, complexing agent, and reducing agent is required to set up a smoothly operating system.

With benzoyl peroxide a system with iron works well. Wall and Swoboda [29] have studied this system and show that oil soluble ferrous ion reacts with benzoyl peroxide to generate radicals. Then the iron(III) goes into the water layer and is complexed (pyrophosphate, oxalate, citrate, etc.), reduced by a water soluble reducing agent such as glucose, and gradually returned to the oil phase as an oil soluble iron salt (iron soap if soap is the emulsifier) to keep regenerating radicals as needed.

In butadiene-styrene polymerization in soap emulsion, the more soluble the hydroperoxide initiator is in oil the more rapidly can the polymerization be achieved. It can be extremely fast (70% conversion in 14 minutes at 0°) if all the variables are adjusted perfectly.[30]

The initiation stage is dependent on temperature if a peroxide is

[28] I. M. Kolthoff, private communication.

[29] F. T. Wall and T. J. Swoboda, *J. Am. Chem. Soc.,* **71,** 919 (1949).

[30] J. R. Miller, CR-3159 (Nov. 7, 1952); J. H. Scarry, CR-3371 (Sept. 15, 1953) (The B. F. Goodrich Company).

used. The redox reaction is very rapid even at low temperatures, hence these systems give rapid low temperature polymerizations.

In addition to organic peroxides and hydroperoxides, a new type of initiator developed in recent years is represented by azobisisobutyronitrile,

$$
\begin{array}{ccc}
& CN & CN \\
CH_3 & | & | \quad CH_3 \\
\diagdown & & \diagup \\
& C-N{=}N-C & \\
\diagup & & \diagdown \\
CH_3 & & CH_3
\end{array}
$$

which decomposes at about 70° at a fairly rapid rate to give

$$
\begin{array}{c}
CN \\
| \\
CH_3-C\cdot \\
| \\
CH_3
\end{array}
$$

radicals. This initiator is synthesized from acetone, hydrogen cyanide, and hydrazine followed by oxidation. By changing the ketone used in the synthesis, azobisnitriles can be produced which give radicals rapidly over the range from room temperature up to 110°.

$$
\begin{array}{ccccc}
CH_2 & CN & NC & CH_2 & \\
\diagup \diagdown & \diagup & \diagdown & \diagup \diagdown & \\
H_2C \quad C & -N{=}N- & C \quad CH_2 & \\
| \quad | & & | \quad | & \\
H_2C \quad CH_2 & & H_2C \quad CH_2 & \\
\diagdown \quad \diagup & & \diagdown \quad \diagup & \\
CH_2 & & CH_2 &
\end{array}
$$

110°

$$
\begin{array}{ccccccc}
CH_3 & & & & & CH_3 \\
| & & & & & | \\
O & & CN & & CN & & O \\
| & & | & & | & & | \\
CH_3-C-CH_2- & C-N{=}N- & C-CH_2- & C-CH_3 \\
| & & | & & | & & | \\
CH_3 & & CH_3 & & CH_3 & & CH_3
\end{array}
$$

Room temperature or below

Methyl neopentyl ketone also gives an active azonitrile at low temperatures. These azonitriles are temperature sensitive initiators, and no redox type activator has been found to work with them.

These few examples do not begin to cover all known initiators. For specific cases many combinations of the agents have been successfully used. But the initiators mentioned above are the common ones in practical use.

5. Chain Transfer Agents

A great many organic molecules react with radicals to give a chain transfer which ends one growing radical chain and starts a new chain growing. In discussing termination an example of chain transfer by a mercaptan was given. This agent is used in synthetic rubber (GR-S) production from butadiene and styrene. Dodecyl mercaptan, $C_{12}H_{25}SH$, has just the right balance of oil and water solubility in soap emulsion to give the right transfer rate for this reaction. For solution or bulk polymerization a very different molecular weight mercaptan might be better.

In addition to mercaptans such materials as dioxane, methylal, chloroform, carbon tetrachloride, and hydrogen chloride show this type of activity. For example,

$$n\text{CH}_2{=}\text{CH}_2 + \text{HCl} \xrightarrow{\text{peroxide}} \text{H}(\text{CH}_2\text{CH}_2)_n\text{Cl}$$

$$n\text{CH}_2{=}\text{CH}_2 + \text{CCl}_4 \xrightarrow{\text{peroxide}} \text{Cl}(\text{CH}_2\text{CH}_2)_n\text{CCl}_3$$

These products are formed by chain transfer.

Aryl disulfides are also effective chain transfer agents. Particular success has been achieved with sterically hindered disulfides in styrene and butadiene polymerizations. There is much difference in the degree of activity of the following four disulfides.

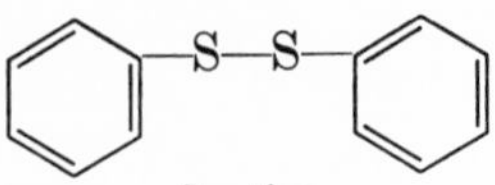

Inactive

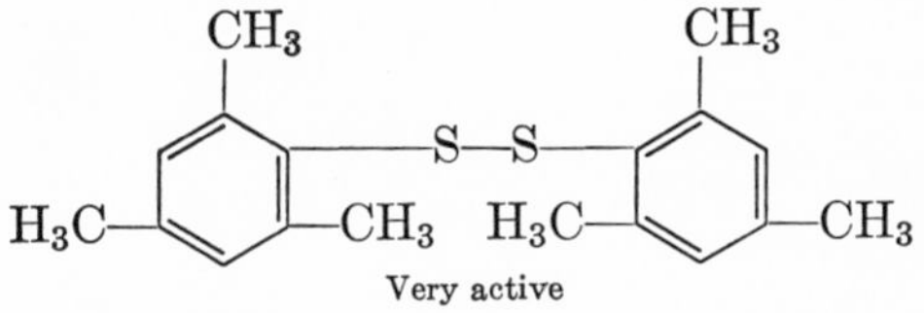

Very active

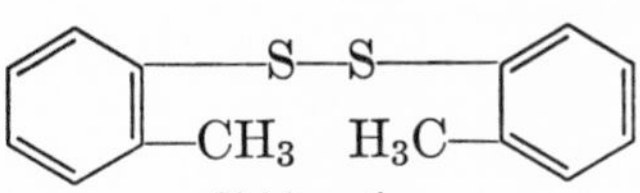

Fairly active

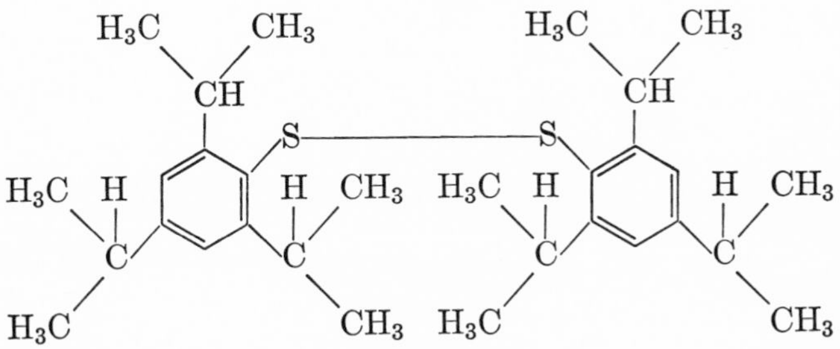

Inactive

Diisopropyl xanthogen disulfide has been developed by the Germans as a chain transfer agent in synthetic rubber manufacture.

$$H_3C \diagdown \underset{\|}{\overset{S}{}} \underset{\|}{\overset{S}{}} CH_3$$

$$CHO-C-S-S-C-O-C-H$$

$$H_3C \diagup CH_3$$

6. Polymer Structure

The free radical mechanism of polymerization which has been postulated would predict that in nearly every case the addition vinyl polymer would have a very regular structure of the "head to tail" type.

$$R \cdot + CH_2{=}CHY \rightarrow RCH_2{-}CHY \cdot \rightarrow R(CH_2CHY)_nCH_2CHY \cdot$$

In the propagation reaction the radical addition to the olefin always proceeds in a manner to give the more stable free radical. Several studies of polymer structure by chemical methods have established that this is the situation. Polyvinyl chloride has the chlorine atoms on alternate carbon atoms. Polyvinyl acetate, polystyrene, polyacrylic esters, and a wide variety of others show this alternating structure. Some cases of structure proof may be cited.

If methyl vinyl ketone is polymerized, the expected head to tail arrangement of units should give a 1,5-diketone. Any "head to head tail to tail" structure would produce a 1,4-diketone. 1,5-Diketones readily undergo an aldol ring closure to give cyclohexenes. 1,4-Diketones undergo ring closure to give furans. The head to tail structure will lead to a poly condensed ring system. Occasional oxygen atoms

will be left where by chance the aldol reaction leaves carbonyls on alternate carbons. Flory [31] has calculated that in a random closure of this type 81.6% of the oxygen should be eliminated.

In the head to head tail to tail structure the reaction would be

[31] P. J. Flory, *J. Am. Chem. Soc.,* **61,** 1518 (1939).

$$-CH_2-CH-CH-CH_2-CH_2-CH-CH-$$

with the pendant groups:

CO CO   CO CO

CH_3 CH_3   CH_3 CH_3

$$\downarrow$$

$$-CH_2-C\!\!=\!\!C-CH_2-CH_2-C\!\!=\!\!C-$$

$$H_3C \diagup O \diagdown CH_3 \quad H_3C \diagup O \diagdown CH_3$$

In this case exactly 50% of the oxygen should be lost by dehydration.

Experimentally it was found that 79 to 85% of the oxygen is lost by dehydration of polymethyl vinyl ketone and that the polymer produced is not crosslinked. This is excellent evidence for the head to tail structure.

Polyvinyl alcohol offers another interesting case because the head to head tail to tail structure leads to 1,2-dihydroxyethane structures and these 1,2-glycols are readily oxidized by periodic acid. The head to tail structure leads to a 1,3-glycol which is not oxidized by this reagent. Early work showed no appreciable reduction of periodic acid by polyvinyl alcohol and hence gave evidence for the 1,3-glycol structure. Flory and Leutner [32] observed that the treatment of polyvinyl alcohol with periodic acid led to a marked reduction in the intrinsic viscosity of its solutions. This means that 1,2-glycol units (or closely related structures) must be present in the alcohol and that some head to head tail to tail arrangement of monomer units must be present in the original polyvinyl acetate from which the polyvinyl alcohol was prepared.

While the major structure of the vinyl polymers is undoubtedly this regular head to tail arrangement of units, we have increasing evidence that there are random units which are not accounted for by this simple head to tail arrangement. There is evidence that polyvinyl chloride

has some tertiary chlorine atoms, $-\overset{\displaystyle |}{\underset{\displaystyle |}{C}}-$. These must be produced by

Cl

a radical rearrangement or a chain transfer reaction during the growth of the polymer chain.

[32] P. J. Flory and F. S. Leutner, *J. Polymer Sci.*, **3**, 880 (1948).

There is also evidence for longer chain branches in polyethylene. A study carried out by chemists at the du Pont Company [33] indicates two kinds of branching in their polyethylenes. They describe them as long chain branching and short chain branching. Long chain branching is caused by intermolecular hydrogen transfer between a completed polyethylene molecule and a growing polyethylene radical.[34]

$$RCH_2CH_2 \cdot + R''CH_2CH_2R'' \rightarrow RCH_2CH_3 + R''\dot{C}HCH_2R''$$

The new growing chain can then grow a new long side chain of $-CH_2CH_2-$ units. This branching occurs in a polymerization process as the concentration of the polymer increases. It is not operating at the beginning of a reaction.

Short chain branching may be caused by an intramolecular hydrogen transfer reaction as pictured here.

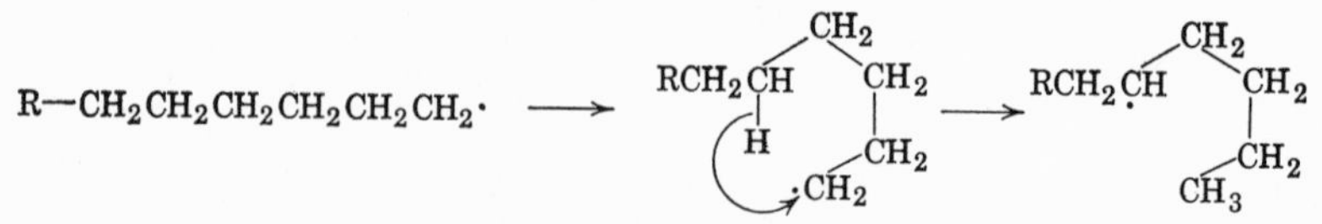

The new propagating chain continues to grow, leaving a side chain of 3 to 5 carbon atoms depending on where hydrogen transfer occurs. Calculations predict that four carbon side chains will be most common followed by C_5 and then C_3. It is also quite probable that some tertiary radicals may form to give units with

$$R-\underset{\underset{C_4H_9}{|}}{\overset{\overset{C_4H_9}{|}}{C}}-$$

quaternary carbon atoms.

A statistical treatment of the whole branching problem indicates that, on a number average molecular weight basis, no more than one long chain branch per polyethylene molecule can be expected and the ratio of short chain branches to long chain branches is about 50:1. These determinations are based on a study of infrared methyl group determinations, light scattering molecular weight studies, inherent viscosity studies, and x-ray studies combined with studies of other physical properties such as hardness, density, and melting point.

---

[33] M. J. Roedel, *J. Am. Chem. Soc.*, **75**, 6110 (1953); W. M. D. Bryant and R. C. Voter, *ibid.*, **75**, 6113 (1953); F. W. Billmeyer, Jr., *ibid.*, **75**, 6118 (1953); J. K. Beasley, *ibid.*, **75**, 6123 (1953); C. A. Sperati, W. A. Franta and H. W. Starkweather, Jr., *ibid.*, **75**, 6127 (1953).

[34] P. J. Flory, *J. Am. Chem. Soc.*, **59**, 241 (1937); **69**, 2893 (1947).

No vinyl polymer other than polyethylene has received such a thorough study of the degree of branching. It seems very probable that there would be much less hydrogen transfer of this nature in most common vinyl polymers because there would be a far greater difference in radical stability between the end radical and a radical in the chain. For example, with methyl methacrylate the radical

$$\underset{CO_2CH_3}{\overset{CH_3}{RCH_2C}}{-\!\!\!-\!\!\!-}\underset{CO_2CH_3}{\overset{CH_3}{CH_2{-}C}}{-\!\!\!-\!\!\!-}\underset{CO_2CH_3}{\overset{CH_3}{CH_2{-}C\cdot}}$$

would be more stable than one such as

$$\underset{CO_2CH_3}{\overset{CH_3}{RCH_2C}}{-\!\!\!-\!\!\!-}\underset{CO_2CH_3}{\overset{CH_3}{CH{-}C}}{-\!\!\!-\!\!\!-}\underset{CO_2CH_3}{\overset{CH_3}{CH_2CH}}$$

because the first radical can be stabilized by resonance with the carbomethoxy group. There are also cases such as vinyl acetate in which chain transfer could be favored because of an activation in the hydrogen in the acetate group.

Other Addition Polymerizations (Free Radical Initiated)

There are other addition polymerization reactions which we discussed under condensation polymerization because of their stepwise character. We know at least one addition polymerization other than vinyl type polymerization which is free radical initiated. This is the reaction between a dimercaptan and a non-conjugated diolefin.

$$n HS(CH_2)_n SH \ + \ n CH_2{=}CH{-}R{-}CH{=}CH_2 \xrightarrow{\text{Persulfate}}$$

$$H \!\!+\!\! S{-}(CH_2)_n{-}S{-}CH_2CH_2R{-}CH_2{-}CH_2 \!\!+\!\!_n H$$

This first reaction is very fast and is followed by a very slow reaction which doubles the molecular weight. The high molecular weight polymer produced in the slow reaction can be reduced with metals and acid to give the lower molecular weight material. It therefore appears that the first polymerization reaction proceeds by a radical mechanism to produce a polymer with a terminal —SH group. This then is slowly oxidized to produce a disulfide link which can be reduced to regenerate the mercaptan. If the polymerization reaction is catalyzed by an azonitrile initiator, the oxidative step does not occur. The —SH end group in the non-oxidized polymer can be oxidized by iodine to give the polymer with one disulfide link.

This reaction between a dimercaptan and a diolefin fails with conjugated diolefins. The first addition does occur between 1,3-butadiene and hexamethylene dimercaptan to give a dicrotyl ether of hexamethylene dithiol.

$$CH_3CH{=}CHCH_2{-}S{-}(CH_2)_6{-}S{-}CH_2CH{=}CHCH_3$$

Further reaction stops because a double bond β-γ to a sulfide link does not readily add a mercaptan group.

Addition Polymerization
(*Ionic Initiation*)

Vinyl Type

Vinyl type polymers can be prepared from certain olefins by ionic initiation, there being both cationic and anionic types. The type of monomer which polymerizes best for each process is different. In general, monomers which have double bonds to which are attached electron-donating groups or, stated in a different way, groups which will stabilize a carbonium ion, polymerize well with a cationic initiator. Conversely, monomers which have double bonds to which are attached electron-withdrawing substituents or groups which will stabilize an anion will work well with an anionic catalyst. In general, it can be said that ionic initiated polymerization is less complicated by side reactions when carried out at extremely low temperatures ($-50°$ to $-100°$). This is largely due to the fact that the activation energy for propagation is usually very small whereas side reactions such as branching, etc., or termination with solvent have higher activation energies and thus these are minimized at low temperatures. In fact, it is almost always found that the lower the temperature, the higher the molecular weight.

1. Cationic Polymerization

Cationic polymerization differs from free radical initiated polymerization especially in the initiation and termination steps. The initiators are Lewis acids, such as boron fluoride, aluminum chloride, titanium tetrachloride, stannic chloride, sulfuric acid, and other strong protonic acids. All of these except possibly the strong protonic acids need a cocatalyst to initiate polymerization. The cocatalyst supplies hydrogen, and the real initiator is believed to be a (H^+) proton in every case. This means that one end group of the polymer produced is a hydrogen atom.

The monomers which polymerize best by cationic initiation are olefins substituted with electron-releasing type groups such as: iso-

butylene, $\underset{CH_3}{\overset{CH_3}{\diagdown}} C{=}CH_2$; styrene, ⬡—CH=CH$_2$; α-methyl styrene,

⬡—$\underset{CH_3}{\overset{C=CH_2}{|}}$; vinyl alkyl ethers, $CH_2{=}CHOR$; and the dienes,

which are to be considered as a separate group. Propylene does not give a high polymer in cationic initiated polymerization. The acrylates, acrylonitrile, and such substituted olefins do not undergo cationic polymerizations to an appreciable extent.

As mentioned before, the polymerization goes most rapidly to give the highest molecular weight materials when conducted at very low temperatures. Isobutylene with boron fluoride at $-100°$ gives a high polymer in a fraction of a second. At room temperatures dimers form slowly.

The mechanism we write for this type of polymerization can be illustrated with isobutylene.

(1) Initiation.

$$CH_2{=}\underset{CH_3}{\overset{CH_3}{C}} \quad + \; BF_3 \cdot H_2O \;\rightarrow\; H{-}CH_2{-}\underset{CH_3}{\overset{CH_3}{C^{\oplus}}}{-}BF_3O\overset{\ominus}{H}$$

(2) Propagation.

$$CH_3-\overset{\overset{\displaystyle CH_3}{|}}{\underset{\underset{\displaystyle CH_3}{|}}{C}}{}^{\oplus}-BF_3O\overset{\ominus}{H} + CH_2=\overset{\overset{\displaystyle CH_3}{|}}{\underset{\underset{\displaystyle CH_3}{|}}{C}} \longrightarrow$$

$$CH_3-\overset{\overset{\displaystyle CH_3}{|}}{\underset{\underset{\displaystyle CH_3}{|}}{C}}-CH_2-\overset{\overset{\displaystyle CH_3}{|}}{\underset{\underset{\displaystyle CH_3}{|}}{C}}{}^{\oplus}-BF_3O\overset{\ominus}{H}$$

(3) Kinetic termination.

$$CH_3-\overset{\overset{\displaystyle CH_3}{|}}{\underset{\underset{\displaystyle CH_3}{|}}{C}}\left(-CH_2-\overset{\overset{\displaystyle CH_3}{|}}{\underset{\underset{\displaystyle CH_3}{|}}{C}}-\right)_{n-1}CH_2-\overset{\overset{\displaystyle CH_3}{|}}{\underset{\underset{\displaystyle CH_3}{|}}{C}}{}^{\oplus} BF_3 O\overset{\ominus}{H} \longrightarrow$$

$$CH_3-\overset{\overset{\displaystyle CH_3}{|}}{\underset{\underset{\displaystyle CH_3}{|}}{C}}\left(-CH_2-\overset{\overset{\displaystyle CH_3}{|}}{\underset{\underset{\displaystyle CH_3}{|}}{C}}-\right)_{n-1}CH_2-\overset{\overset{\displaystyle CH_2}{||}}{\underset{\underset{\displaystyle CH_3}{|}}{C}} + BF_3 \cdot H_2O$$

(4) Chain transfer with monomer.

$$CH_3-\overset{\overset{\displaystyle CH_3}{|}}{\underset{\underset{\displaystyle CH_3}{|}}{C}}\left(-CH_2-\overset{\overset{\displaystyle CH_3}{|}}{\underset{\underset{\displaystyle CH_3}{|}}{C}}-\right)_{n-1}CH_2-\overset{\overset{\displaystyle CH_3}{|}}{\underset{\underset{\displaystyle CH_3}{|}}{C}}{}^{\oplus} BF_3 O\overset{\ominus}{H} + CH_2=\overset{\underset{\underset{\displaystyle CH_3}{|}}{}}{C}-CH_3 \longrightarrow$$

$$CH_3-\overset{\overset{\displaystyle CH_3}{|}}{\underset{\underset{\displaystyle CH_3}{|}}{C}}\left(-CH_2-\overset{\overset{\displaystyle CH_3}{|}}{\underset{\underset{\displaystyle CH_3}{|}}{C}}-\right)_{n-1}CH_2-\overset{\overset{\displaystyle CH_2}{||}}{\underset{\underset{\displaystyle CH_3}{|}}{C}} + H-CH_2-\overset{\overset{\displaystyle CH_3}{|}}{\underset{\underset{\displaystyle CH_3}{|}}{C}}{}^{\oplus} BF_3 O\overset{\ominus}{H}$$

When a covalent bond can readily form, part of the termination may occur by ion combination. An example of this type is the polymerization of styrene with trifluoroacetic acid.[35]

$$H\left(-CH_2-\overset{\underset{\underset{\displaystyle C_6H_5}{|}}{}}{CH}-\right)_n CH_2-\overset{\underset{\underset{\displaystyle C_6H_5}{|}}{}}{CH}{}^{\oplus}\quad CF_3COO^{\ominus} \longrightarrow$$

$$H\left(-CH_2-\overset{\underset{\underset{\displaystyle C_6H_5}{|}}{}}{CH}-\right)_n CH_2-\overset{\underset{\underset{\displaystyle C_6H_5}{|}}{}}{CH}-O-\overset{\overset{\displaystyle O}{||}}{C}-CF_3$$

[35] J. J. Throssell, S. P. Wood, M. Szwarc, and V. Stannett, *J. Am. Chem. Soc.*, **78**, 1122 (1956).

Excess moisture interferes with the polymerization, although as noted a small amount of water functions as a cocatalyst. High temperatures reduce the molecular weight of the polymer even more rapidly than in radical initiated polymerization. Other proton-furnishing cocatalysts will act with Friedel-Crafts type catalysts to initiate polymerization. Different catalysts show best activity at different temperatures with the same olefin. It has been shown that an increase in the dielectric constant of the medium increases both rate and degree of polymerization.[36]

One important technical detail in performing this type of reaction is the use of a low boiling solvent such as ethylene which will keep the polymerizing mixture cold by evaporating at the desired temperature.

2. Anionic Polymerization

Beaman [37] showed that sodium in liquid ammonia at $-75°$ was a particularly effective initiator for the polymerization of α-methylacrylonitrile. This was the first case of anionic chain polymerization which was recognized. He also found that acrylonitrile, methyl acrylate, and methyl methacrylate were polymerized by this combination of reagents. Other anionic initiators which he observed were Grignard reagents and triphenylmethyl sodium.

Higginson and Wooding [38] investigated the kinetics of the polymerization of styrene with potassium amide in liquid ammonia. They decided that the mechanism could best be explained as follows.

$$KNH_2 \rightleftharpoons K^\oplus + NH_2^\ominus$$

$$NH_2^\ominus + M \rightarrow NH_2M^\ominus$$

$$NH_2M^\ominus + nM \rightarrow NH_2(M)nM^\ominus$$

$$NH_2(M)nM^\ominus + NH_3 \rightarrow NH_2(M)nMH + NH_2^\ominus$$

It has been known that dienes, particularly 1,3-butadiene and isoprene, can be polymerized by alkali metals and alkali metal alkyls. These reactions may also be anionic in character. One piece of evidence to separate anionic from radical polymerization is that these ionic polymerizations are not inhibited by t-butyl catechol, which destroys free radicals. The diene polymerization is discussed later.

[36] D. D. Pepper, *Trans. Faraday Soc.*, **45**, 397 (1949).
[37] R. G. Beaman, *J. Am. Chem. Soc.*, **70**, 3115 (1948).
[38] W. C. E. Higginson and N. S. Wooding, *J. Chem. Soc.*, **1952**, 1760.

At the present time no anionic vinyl polymerizations are carried out on a practical scale. They share with cationic polymerizations the property of proceeding more readily at very low temperatures.

Cyclic Monomers

A variety of cyclic monomers can be caused to polymerize to linear polymers. The exact mechanisms of most of these transformations have not been worked out. Yet there is little doubt that they represent a type of ionic initiation. We will not attempt to subdivide these cases into anionic and cationic initiation but will consider them on the basis of the chemical nature of the monomers and polymers.

$$\text{Cyclic ethers} \rightarrow \text{Polyethers}$$

$$\text{Cyclic amines} \rightarrow \text{Polyamines}$$

$$\text{Cyclic esters} \rightarrow \text{Polyesters}$$

$$\text{Lactams} \rightarrow \text{Polyamides}$$

$$\text{Carboanhydrides} \rightarrow \text{Polyamides}$$

1. Polyethers

Ethylene oxide, $H_2C\!\!-\!\!CH_2$, may be polymerized to polyethylene

oxides by a variety of methods and conditions. The reaction is catalyzed by traces of either acids or bases. Moisture seems to be an essential component but is needed only in trace amounts. The polymers are linear polyethers and many are water soluble.

$$n CH_2\!\!-\!\!CH_2 \xrightarrow{\;H_2O\;} H\text{-}(OCH_2CH_2\text{-})_n OH$$

The reaction is apparently first opening of a ring to ethylene glycol or an ionic species related thereto and then further reaction of ethylene oxide. Water furnishes the end group of the polymer, which is really a polyethylene glycol.

Tetrahydrofuran has also been caused to undergo polymerization by the action of acids. A German patent covers its conversion to a polymer by the action of antimony pentachloride.

$$n\; \text{[cyclic structure]} \xrightarrow{\;SbCl_5\;} \text{-}(OCH_2\!\!-\!\!CH_2\!\!-\!\!CH_2\!\!-\!\!CH_2\text{-})_n$$

It seems probable that H and OH are the end groups. "Adiprene" is a condensation product of this type of polymer with a diisocyanate.

Trimethylene oxide can also be made to polymerize, but little work has been done on the reaction because the monomer is too hard to obtain.

Price and Osgan [39] have shown that stereospecific polymerization of propylene oxide can be attained by use of ferric chloride catalysts, whereas with potassium hydroxide catalysis a non-stereospecific polymerization occurs. Thus with *dl*-propylene oxide and potassium hydroxide a liquid polymer is formed, whereas from *l*-propylene oxide a crystalline polymer is formed. With ferric chloride catalysis, both *l*- and *dl*-propylene oxides yield crystalline polymers.

2. Polyamines

Ethyleneimine can be easily polymerized by the action of acid catalysts [40] to yield a poly secondary amine.

$$n CH_2—CH_2 \underset{NH}{\diagdown\diagup} \longrightarrow \left(CH_2—CH_2—\underset{|}{\overset{H}{N}} \right)_n$$

The end groups postulated by Jones are

$$\underset{CH_2}{\overset{CH_2}{\diagdown}} N— \quad \text{and} \quad H$$

3. Polyesters

Carothers investigated the transformation of cyclic esters, lactones, and lactides to linear polymers and discussed them in his article in *Chemical Reviews*.[5] He pointed out that six-membered cyclic esters are particularly prone to rearrange (ester interchange) to produce linear polyesters, and he related the ease of this reaction to the ease of hydrolysis of the cyclic ester.

$$n CH_2—CH_2—CH_2—CH_2—C{=}O \underset{O}{\rule{0pt}{0pt}} \xrightarrow{HOH} H \left(OCH_2CH_2CH_2 \overset{O}{\overset{\diagup\!\diagup}{C}} \right)_n OH$$

[39] C. C. Price and M. Osgan, *J. Am. Chem. Soc.*, **78**, 4787 (1956).
[40] G. D. Jones et al., *J. Org. Chem.*, **9**, 125 (1944).

A molecule of water seems to open the lactone to give the hydroxy acid, and ester interchange can account for the rest of the polymerization. It seems to be an ionic reaction.

$$n \begin{matrix} CH_2-O-C=O \\ | \quad\quad | \\ CH_2-O-C=O \end{matrix} \longrightarrow \left(\begin{matrix} O \quad O \\ \| \quad \| \\ -OC-C-O-CH_2-CH_2- \end{matrix} \right)_n$$

Ethylene oxalate   Polyethylene oxalate

$$n \begin{matrix} CH_2-O \\ | \\ CH_2 \quad\quad C=O \\ | \\ CH_2-O \end{matrix} \longrightarrow \left(\begin{matrix} O \\ \| \\ -O-C-O-CH_2-CH_2-CH_2- \end{matrix} \right)_n$$

Trimethylene carbonate   Polytrimethylene carbonate

$$n O \begin{matrix} CH_2-C \nearrow^O \\ \quad\quad\quad\searrow O \\ C-CH_2 \\ O \end{matrix} \longrightarrow \left(\begin{matrix} O \quad\quad\quad O \\ \| \quad\quad\quad \| \\ -O-CH_2-C-O-CH_2-C- \end{matrix} \right)_n$$

Glycolid

None of these polyesters has become of practical value.

To date, the reaction has not been successfully applied to five-membered cyclic esters, and little has been done with rings of more than six members.

4. Polyamides

The conversion of caprolactam to the linear polymer of ε-aminocaproic acid is one of the most important rearrangements of a cyclic amide to linear polyamide. The polymerization step is catalyzed by

$$\begin{matrix} O \\ \| \\ C \\ \diagdown NH \end{matrix} \longrightarrow \left(\begin{matrix} H \quad\quad O \\ | \quad\quad \| \\ -N(CH_2)_5C- \end{matrix} \right)_n$$

moisture, by metallic sodium, and possibly by other catalysts of the acid or base type.

There are very few well-authenticated cases of conversion of six-membered ring amides to linear polyamides. Some evidence of the conversion of diketopiperazines to linear polyamides is given in the early literature, but little work has been published since polymer chemistry became better understood.[41]

More work has been done on the N-carboanhydrides of α-amino acids. Leuchs discussed this reaction for the glycine derivatives in

$$
n \quad
\begin{matrix}
CH_2\!-\!C\!\!\!\diagup^{\displaystyle O} \\
| \qquad\qquad\diagdown O \\
N\!-\!\!-\!C\!\!\!\diagup \\
| \qquad\qquad\diagdown O \\
H
\end{matrix}
\quad\longrightarrow\quad
\left(\!\!\begin{matrix} H \\ | \\ N\!-\!CH_2\!-\!C\!\!\!\diagup^{\displaystyle O} \\ \end{matrix}\!\!\right)_{\!n} + nCO_2
$$

1906,[13] and Curtius and Sieber extended it to other amino acid derivatives in 1922.[42] It was reactivated in 1947 and has been extended by Woodward and Schamm,[43] Katchalski et al.,[44] Hanby et al.,[45] and a group at the du Pont Company [46] to a variety of other α-amino acid derivatives. Some of the polyamides thus prepared are soluble and make good films and fibers. None has become sufficiently interesting for commercial development.

There are also patents covering the conversion of the five-membered cyclic amide of pyrrolidone to a linear polyamide.[47]

$$
n \quad
\begin{matrix}
 \\
\diagup\!\!\diagdown NH \\
C \\
\| \\
O
\end{matrix}
\quad\longrightarrow\quad
(\!-NH\!-\!CH_2CH_2CH_2\!-\!CO\!-\!)_{\!n}
$$

These are all polymerized by ionic means, but not much detail has been published on mechanisms.

[41] K. Shibata, *Acta Phytochim. (Japan)*, **2**, 39 (1925); **2**, 193 (1926).

[42] T. Curtius and W. Sieber, *Ber.*, **55**, 1543 (1922).

[43] R. B. Woodward and C. H. Schamm, *J. Am. Chem. Soc.*, **69**, 1551 (1947).

[44] E. Katchalski, I. Crassfeld, and M. Frankel, *J. Am. Chem. Soc.*, **69**, 2564 (1947).

[45] W. E. Hanby, S. G. Waley, and J. Watson, *Nature*, **101**, 132 (1948).

[46] U.S. Patents 2,517,610 (Aug. 8, 1950); 2,534,283 (Aug. 19, 1950); 2,560,584 (1951); 2,572,844 (1951); 2,608,548 (1952).

[47] W. O. Ney, Jr., W. R. Nummy, and C. E. Barnes, U.S. Patent 2,638,463, *C.A.*, **47**, 9624 (1953); C. E. Barnes, French Patent 1,093,850 (1955); W. O. Ney, Jr., French Patent 1,093,851 (1955).

New Ionic Systems

Morton [48] has developed a combination of allylsodium and sodium isopropoxide known as the Alfin catalyst which is unique as a polymerization catalyst for dienes such as butadiene or isoprene. This seems to be an anionic type of initiation, although Morton later favored the view that initiation is of the free radical type. This point will be referred to again when diene polymerization is discussed. For the Alfin catalyst to perform best, it is necessary that allylsodium and sodium isopropoxide be used in exactly equimolar proportions. Also, some sodium chloride must be present. The catalyst system seems to be complex, and the polymerization is apparently on crystal surfaces. In this respect this catalyst seems closely related to newer Ziegler type catalysts.

The several new processes which have been developed for the low pressure polymerization of ethylene [49-51] have opened up a new era in polymerization chemistry.

The Phillips Petroleum Company [49] process of low pressure polymerization of ethylene utilizes a chromium catalyst on a silica-alumina support and operates at a temperature of 135–190° with just enough pressure to keep the operating hydrocarbon solvent in the liquid phase.

The process of the Standard Oil Company of Indiana, which utilizes a catalyst system of reduced metal oxides of Subgroup V on silica or chromium oxide support, operates in a temperature range of 130–260° and pressure of 200–5000 pounds per square inch with hydrocarbon solvents.

The process developed in the laboratory of Karl Ziegler at Mühlheim makes use of a catalyst prepared usually from aluminum alkyls and titanium tetrachloride in a hydrocarbon solvent, and operates at atmospheric pressure and room temperature.

All three of these processes operate under a variety of conditions with catalysts prepared in a variety of ways. They all produce a

[48] A. A. Morton, E. E. Magat, and R. L. Letsinger, *J. Am. Chem. Soc.*, **69**, 950 (1947).

[49] G. C. Bailey and J. A. Reid, U.S. Patents 2,581,228 (1952), 2,606,940 (1952); J. P. Hogan, U.S. Patent 2,642,467 (1953); A. Clark, U.S. Patent 2,706,211 (1955).

[50] (a) E. Field and M. Feller, U.S. Patent 2,691,647 (1954); E. F. Peters, U.S. Patents 2,692,259 (1954), 2,292,295 (1954). (b) E. F. Peters and B. L. Evening, U.S. Patents 2,658,059 (1953), 2,692,261 (1954). (c) A. Zletz, U.S. Patent 2,692,257 (1954).

[51] K. Ziegler, E. Holzkamp, H. Breil, and H. Martin, *Angew. Chem.*, **67**, 541 (1955); K. Ziegler, Belgian Patent 713,081 (1954); *C.A.*, **49**, 3576 (1955).

linear polyethylene of high density and with a molecular weight in the 300,000 range.

Anderson and Merchling [52] have described the polymerization of bicyclo-[2,2,1]-2-heptene with lithium aluminum isobutyl [LiAl(C₄H₉)₄] and titanium tetrachloride. A variety of other metal alkyls and metal hydrides are also effective.

Natta [53] has developed the Ziegler technique and shows that highly crystalline polypropylenes, poly-α-butenes, and polystyrenes, called isotactic polymers, can be prepared. These polymers have a regular stereochemical configuration. Polystyrene prepared by free radical initiated polymerizaton usually melts a little above 100°, whereas Natta's isotactic polystyrene melts above 200°.

Natta has been able to prepare three general types of polymers from terminal monoölefins (RCH=CH₂), depending on the conditions used. The isotactic polymers are believed to have all the R groups arranged regularly on one side of the zigzag backbone chain of the polymer. The polymers which he designates as syndiotactic have the R groups also arranged in a regular manner, but they are alternately above and below the plane of the backbone chain of the polymer. The third type of polymer, or atactic polymer, has a random arrangement of the R groups about the plane of the backbone chain, which is the type of polymer usually obtained in free radical polymerizations.

In general, monosubstituted olefins of the type RCH=CH₂ are polymerized by the Ziegler catalysts. The olefin should not be branched closer than the 3- or 4-position with respect to the double bond. Homopolymerizations seem to proceed more readily than do copolymerization reactions. Up to the present time no satisfactory method of polymerizing olefins with functional groups such as halogen, carbonyl, and nitrile has been described, although there are persistent rumors that such polymerizations have been performed.

These new catalysts have opened up the field of hydrocarbon polymers from substituted ethylenes which do not polymerize under free radical initiation conditions. An excellent review of the status of the development is presented by Stille.[54]

Much has been written about the mechanisms of these new catalytic procedures for producing polymers of hydrocarbons. The reaction of an aluminum alkyl with titanium tetrachloride is believed to cause

[52] A. W. Anderson and W. G. Merchling, U.S. Patent 2,721,189 (1955).

[53] G. Natta, *Chim. e ind. (Milan)*, **37**, 888 (1955); *J. Polymer Sci.*, **16**, 143 (1955).

[54] J. K. Stille, *Chem. Revs.*, **58**, 541 (1958).

reduction of the titanium [55] and also probably some alkylation to yield titanium alkyls.[56] These facts seem to be in fairly general agreement with the view that the active catalyst is not soluble in the hydrocarbon phase and that the polymerization occurs on a surface. The nature of this surface has much to do with the stereochemical nature of the product obtained. The fact that ethylene can be polymerized at atmospheric pressure is significant. In the free radical initiated high pressure polymerization of ethylene, the pressure seems to be needed to ensure a high concentration of ethylene around the growing polyethylene radical to prevent this active radical from terminating growth by some coupling or chain transfer. This new low pressure process seems to hold the active growing center of the polyethylene chain in some sort of coordination with the catalyst surface sufficiently stabilized to survive until more ethylene arrives at the reaction scene.

It seems probable that the active catalyst in the process of the Standard Oil Company of Indiana acts in a similar manner in forming some coordination complex with the growing polymer chain.

The Phillips process is believed to involve a different mechanism but also involves a surface complex of hydrocarbon, polymer, and chromium oxide which gives the needed life to the growing chain so that high ethylene concentrations are not critical.

Polyaldehydes, Polyacetals, and Polymercaptals

The polymerization of formaldehyde to paraformaldehyde is undoubtedly an ionic initiated polymerization.[57]

$$nCH_2O \longrightarrow -(CH_2O)_n-$$

Staudinger's early work on polyoxymethylene was one of the studies which established the fact that polymers are really macromolecules held together with ordinary valence forces. He demonstrated that there are many polyoxymethylenes with a variety of end groups such as H and OH, H and OCH_3, CH_3O and CH_3. The fact that this is an ionic initiated polymerization had not been stressed in publications, but there seems to be little doubt of this fact.

[55] D. B. Ludlum, A. W. Anderson, and C. E. Ashby, *J. Am. Chem. Soc.*, **80**, 1380 (1958).

[56] H. N. Friedlander and K. Oita, *Ind. Eng. Chem.*, **49**, 1885 (1957).

[57] du Pont, British Patents 702,097 (1955) and 742,135 (1955).

Acetaldehyde gives mainly a dimer when it polymerizes, but the solid metaldehyde which has sometimes been called a tetramer may be a polymeric material. The evidence is not conclusive.

Ciamician[58] reported a polymer of benzaldehyde made by exposure of benzaldehyde to sunlight. It is a powdery material which has not received much study, and its structure has never been determined.

Carothers made polyacetals by acetal exchange between formals and glycols promoted by ionic catalysis with Lewis acids. None of

$$CH_2(OC_4H_9)_2 + HO(CH_2)_nOH \xrightarrow{FeCl_3} \left[CH_2O-(CH_2)_nO\right]_n + 2C_4H_9OH$$

these polymers has attained practical significance. They tend to revert to macrocyclic acetals rather readily.

Aldehydes and ketones react readily with hexamethylene dimercaptan under acidic conditions to yield polymercaptals or polymercaptols. The reaction proceeds rapidly at low temperatures, as is characteristic of ionic reactions.

$$nC_6H_5CHO + nHS(CH_2)_6SH \xrightarrow[\text{or HCl}]{FeCl_3} \left[\begin{matrix} C_6H_5 \\ | \\ C-S-(CH_2)_6-S \\ | \\ H \end{matrix}\right]_n + nH_2O$$

With decamethylene dimercaptan a cyclic dimer is obtained instead

$$2C_6H_5C\overset{O}{\underset{H}{\big\|}} + 2HS-(CH_2)_{10}SH \rightarrow$$

$$C_6H_5CH\underset{S-(CH_2)_{10}-S}{\overset{S-(CH_2)_{10}-S}{\big<}}CHC_6H_5 + 2H_2O$$

of the polymer. This reaction of decamethylene dimercaptan occurs with other aldehydes and some ketones. The cyclic material is formed without any special conditions of reaction such as high dilution.

[58] G. Ciamician and P. Silber, *Ber.*, **42**, 1386 (1909); L. Mascarelli, *Atti accad. nazl. Lincei*, **19**, I, 383 (1910); L. Mascarelli and N. Bossinelli, *ibid.*, **19**, I, 562 (1910); *C.A.*, **4**, 2457 (1910); L. Mascarelli, *Atti accad. nazl. Lincei*, **19**, II, 239 (1910); *C.A.*, **5**, 278 (1911).

Autenrieth and Beutell [59] reported a similar cyclization in the reaction between acetone and m- and p-xylyl dimercaptans, but these large and unusual rings were apparently overlooked when big ring chemistry was reinvestigated.

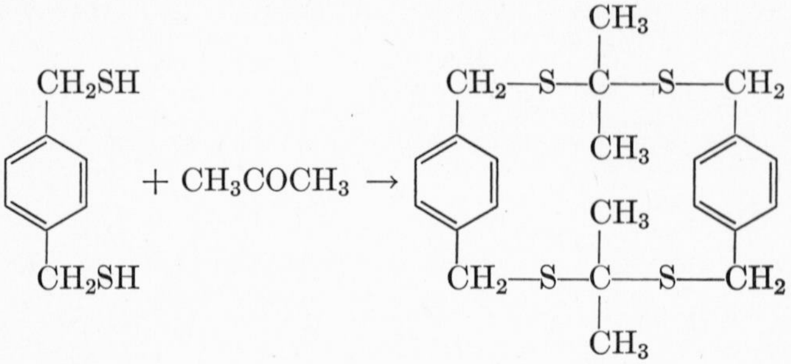

$$
\begin{array}{c}
\text{CH}_2\text{SH} \\
\bigotimes \\
\text{CH}_2\text{SH}
\end{array}
+ \text{CH}_3\text{COCH}_3 \rightarrow
$$

Copolymerization

Copolymerization is a term which is usually restricted to the polymerization of two or more vinyl monomers to give chains which contain all the monomer units arranged along the chain in a random manner. We shall discuss primarily the case of only two monomers because otherwise the situation becomes extremely complicated.

It should be pointed out that copolymers can be made by condensation reactions, but usually the term copolymer is not applied in that case. Hence we think of vinyl type polymers when this subject is considered.

Reactivity Ratios

Not all types of vinyl monomers undergo copolymerization. When they do, there are four chain propagating reactions that can occur in a mixture of monomers M_1 and M_2.

---

[59] W. Autenrieth and F. Beutell, *Ber.*, **42**, 4346, 4357 (1909).

$$M_1\cdot \;+\; M_1 \xrightarrow{k_{11}} (M_1)_2\cdot$$

$$M_1\cdot \;+\; M_2 \xrightarrow{k_{12}} M_1M_2\cdot$$

$$M_2\cdot \;+\; M_2 \xrightarrow{k_{22}} (M_2)_2\cdot$$

$$M_2\cdot \;+\; M_1 \xrightarrow{k_{21}} M_2M_1\cdot$$

where k_{11} is the rate constant for an M_1 radical to add to monomer M_1
k_{12} is the rate constant for an M_1 radical to add to monomer M_2
k_{22} is the rate constant for an M_2 radical to add to monomer M_2
k_{21} is the rate constant for an M_2 radical to add to monomer M_1.

Mayo and Walling have developed the necessary equations and laboratory procedures for the determination of the reactivity ratios for copolymerizations of many monomers.[60]

$$r_1 = \frac{k_{11}}{k_{12}} \qquad r_2 = \frac{k_{22}}{k_{21}}$$

If copolymerizations are run with different mixtures of monomers, stopped after an extremely low yield of polymer is obtained, and the composition of this polymer is determined, it is possible to determine these reactivity ratios. By substituting the proper experimental values for M_1, M_2 (moles of monomer M_1 and M_2 respectively in the feed), m_1 and m_2 (moles of monomer M_1 and M_2 respectively in the polymer) in the equation

$$r_2 = \frac{M_1}{M_2}\left[\frac{m_2}{m_1}\left(1 + \frac{M_1}{M_2}r_1\right) - 1\right]$$

linear equations containing the reactivity ratios r_1 and r_2 are obtained. These are solved graphically. Such values are helpful in determining the proper ratios of monomers needed in a charging stock to yield a copolymer at a definite conversion which will have the desired ratio of individual monomer units. The values are also helpful in making predictions of copolymerizations which are possible.

The ideal behavior of monomers gives the value $r_1 = 1/r_2$, but this is the exceptional case. Many monomers which have little or no tendency to homopolymerize will copolymerize. Some pairs of monomers tend to copolymerize in a 1:1 molecular ratio. Some pairs of monomers which homopolymerize do not copolymerize with each other.

[60] F. Mayo and C. Walling, *Chem. Revs.*, **46**, 191 (1950).

TABLE 1. REACTIVITY RATIOS OF TYPICAL BINARY
MIXTURES OF OLEFINS

M_1	M_2	r_1	r_2	$r_1 r_2$
Styrene	Butadiene	0.78	1.39	1.08
Styrene	p-Methoxystyrene	1.16	0.82	0.95
Styrene	Vinyl acetate	55	0.01	—
Vinyl acetate	Vinyl chloride	0.23	1.68	0.39
Vinyl acetate	Dimethyl maleate	0.17	0.043	0.007
Maleic anhydride	Isopropenyl acetate	0.002	0.032	—
Methyl acrylate	Vinyl chloride	9.0	0.083	0.75

Some typical binary mixtures which have been studied are listed in Table 1, and the results are discussed to show how the data may be used. The first two pairs behave ideally. In the case of maleic anhydride and isopropenyl acetate the reactivity ratios are very low, and this means that the pair tends to give a copolymer of a 1:1 molecular ratio over a wide range of monomer compositions. Vinyl acetate and diethyl maleate have the same tendency, although a vinyl acetate end group will add vinyl acetate monomer even in the presence of diethyl maleate.

Styrene and vinyl acetate essentially will not copolymerize since styrene is about ten times as reactive as is vinyl acetate toward styrene radical. Small amounts of styrene act as an inhibitor to vinyl acetate polymerization because a vinyl acetate radical will add styrene ten times faster than vinyl acetate, so addition occurs and the low tendency of the styrene end radical to add vinyl acetate inhibits the polymerization reaction.

The effect of temperature on reactivity ratios is small. The type of polymerization system, initiator, etc., also has little or no effect. There is a very great difference, however, if instead of a free radical system one uses cationic or anionic type initiation.

Some ionic copolymerization results are listed in Table 2. Because the ionic systems fail to copolymerize so often, not many data have become available.

Walling and Mayo [61] have arrived at the following order of reactivity in cationic polymerization:

Vinyl ether > Isobutylene > α-Methylstyrene >
Isoprene > Styrene > Butadiene

[61] C. Walling, E. L. Omiggs, W. Cummings, and F. R. Mayo, *J. Am. Chem. Soc.*, **72**, 48 (1950).

For anionic polymerization they list the order as

Acrylonitrile > Methacrylonitrile > Methyl methacrylate > Styrene > Butadiene

Styrene and the dienes are unique in being susceptible to initiation by all three types of initiators. It should be pointed out that the Walling and Mayo rates are propagation rates. Sometimes reactivity ratios are useful in determining what mechanism of initiation of polymerization is operative under a given set of conditions. Thus, if a mixture of styrene and methyl methacrylate is polymerized by free radical initiation, the polymer formed will contain both monomers. If initiation is by a cationic mechanism, only polystyrene is produced. If initiation is by an anionic mechanism, only polymethyl methacrylate results.

Copolymerizable Monomers Which Do Not Homopolymerize

It is very difficult to list all olefinic types which copolymerize but do not homopolymerize. Again the comonomer also is important in

TABLE 2. IONIC REACTIVITY RATIOS

Cationic

M_1	M_2	r_1	r_2	r_1r_2	Radical r_1r_2
Styrene	Methyl methacrylate	10.5 ($\pm$0.2)	0.1 ($\pm$0.05)	0.5–1.5	24
Styrene	Vinyl acetate	8.2 ($\pm$0.1)	0 ($\pm$0.03)	0 –0.25	
Styrene	p-Chlorostyrene	2.7 ($\pm$0.3)	0.35 ($\pm$0.05)	0.7–1.2	0.8

Anionic

M_1	M_2	r_1	r_2	r_1r_2	Radical r_1r_2
Methyl methacrylate	Styrene	6.4 ($\pm$0.1)	0.12 ($\pm$0.05)	0.4–1.1	0.24
Methyl methacrylate	Vinyl acetate	3.2 ($\pm$0.1)	0.4 ($\pm$0.2)	0.4–2.5	>0.3

determining the list, and it is essential to keep this in mind. Styrene is a monomer which copolymerizes with most of the other monomers, and in the discussion here it can be used as a test monomer to determine if another vinyl derivative will copolymerize with it.

In listing the monomers which polymerize in free radical systems it was stated that only $-\overset{\displaystyle |}{\text{C}}=\text{CH}_2$ groups usually would react and that not all of them would polymerize. The monomers which copolymerize but do not homopolymerize are usually disubstituted olefins of the RCH=CHR type. Some of the compounds of interest are

$$
\begin{array}{ccc}
\text{CH}=\text{CH} & & \\
\underset{\text{O}}{\overset{|}{\text{C}}}\diagdown\underset{\text{O}}{}\diagup\underset{\text{O}}{\overset{|}{\text{C}}} & \quad\quad \underset{\underset{\text{O}}{\|}}{\text{CH}_3\text{OC}}\text{—CH} & \quad\quad \underset{\underset{\text{O}}{\|}}{\text{HC}}\text{—CO}_2\text{CH}_3 \\
& \underset{\underset{\text{O}}{\|}}{\text{CH}_3\text{OC}}\text{—CH} & \text{CH}_3\text{O}_2\text{C}\text{—CH}
\end{array}
$$

trans-isomers of

$$\text{C}_6\text{H}_5\text{CH}=\text{CHCN}, \qquad \text{C}_6\text{H}_5\text{CH}=\text{CHCO}_2\text{CH}_3,$$

$$\text{C}_6\text{H}_5\text{CH}=\overset{\overset{\displaystyle O}{\|}}{\text{CH}}\text{CCH}_3, \qquad \text{C}_6\text{H}_5\text{CH}=\text{CH}\text{—}\overset{\overset{\displaystyle O}{\|}}{\text{C}}\text{C}_6\text{H}_5,$$

and the related furyl and thienyl derivatives of the types

$$\text{C}_6\text{H}_5\overset{\overset{\displaystyle O}{\|}}{\text{C}}\text{CH}=\text{CH}\overset{\overset{\displaystyle O}{\|}}{\text{C}}\text{C}_6\text{H}_5 \qquad \text{C}_6\text{H}_5\overset{\overset{\displaystyle O}{\|}}{\text{C}}\text{CH}=\text{CHCO}_2\text{CH}_3$$

but not

$$
\begin{array}{c}
\text{CO}_2\text{CH}_3 \\
| \\
\text{CH}_2 \\
| \\
\underset{\underset{\text{O}}{\|}}{\text{C}}\text{—CO}_2\text{CH}_3 \\
\text{CH}_3\text{O}_2\text{CCH}
\end{array}
$$

This is by no means an inclusive list, but it does indicate types which have been recently added to possible monomers for copolymerization by free radical initiation.

In this list of materials which copolymerize but do not homopolymerize sulfur dioxide may be included. We have no known polymers of sulfur dioxide, yet it does enter into polymerization reactions with 1-olefins and a few disubstituted olefins, $\begin{matrix} R \\ \diagdown \\ \diagup \\ R \end{matrix}$ C=CHR, where R is the methyl group or hydrogen. Even 2-pentene will copolymerize. This is a free radical catalyzed reaction and leads to a polysulfone. The

$$RCH{=}CH_2 \;+\; SO_2 \;\longrightarrow\; \left(\begin{matrix} R \\ | \\ CH-CH_2-SO_2 \end{matrix}\right)_n$$

polymers have received extensive study because they are made from such cheap raw materials. They fail in practice because of heat and alkali sensitivity.

Monomer Reactivity in Copolymerization

Mayo and Walling [60] have arranged some common monomers in a table in order of decreasing activity toward any given radical. This tabulation indicates that a substituent such as C_6H_5 on the olefin has the greatest effect in increasing the reactivity toward attacking radicals. Following this in decreasing value are the groups —CH=CH$_2$, $-\overset{\displaystyle O}{\overset{\|}{C}}-CH_3$, —CN, $-\overset{\displaystyle O}{\overset{\|}{C}}-OR$, Cl, —OCOCH$_3$, and —OR. In fact the last group, the vinyl ethers, rarely copolymerize well with free radical initiators.

The order of reactivity can be correlated with the stabilization of the new radical due to resonance. Thus, when M· adds to styrene, the adduct can be written as the radical

$$M{-}CH_2{-}CH\cdot$$

or in three quinoid structures

$M—CH_2—CH$ $\qquad$ $M—CH_2—CH$ $\qquad$ $M—CH_2—CH$

This resonance stabilizes the radical by some 20 kcal.

This radical stability plays an important part in determining which monomers will copolymerize. When the radical stabilities of two monomers differ greatly as, for example, in the case of styrene,

$—\overset{\cdot}{C}HCH_2R$, and vinyl acetate, $R—CH_2—\overset{\cdot}{C}HOCOCH_3$, little

copolymerization can be achieved.

Block Polymers [62]

When two monomers such as vinyl monomers are copolymerized, the polymer produced may be a regular ordered polymer such as ABABAB, etc. This happens in the relatively few cases where A radical adds to B monomer faster than to A monomer, and B radical adds to A monomer faster than to B monomer. Styrene and maleic anhydride form this type of copolymer. Sulfur dioxide and olefins also alternate in this manner.

More commonly we have a random arrangement of units, ABAABBAAB, etc., where the reactivity ratios and the concentrations regulate the structure of the chain.

Recently chemists have become interested in another type of isomeric arrangement of monomer units called block arrangement. In these so-called block polymers the arrangement of the A and B units are in long blocks

$$A ------- A -- B ------- B -- A ------- A, \quad \text{etc.}$$

Not much is known yet about this type of polymer because it is difficult to prepare one in vinyl polymerization. Some progress is, however, being made in this field, and considerable progress is being made in the condensation polymer field.

[62] V. E. H. Immergut and H. Mark, *Makromol. Chem.*, **18/19**, 322 (1956), have an excellent summary on graft and block polymers.

Melville and his group in England are working on block polymers of the vinyl type.[63] They have devised an apparatus for initiating a flowing solution of monomer and photosensitizer in a capillary tube so that polymerization begins and produces a fairly high concentration of growing chains. This solution flows into a well-agitated large volume of a second monomer, and the polymer continues to grow in size by adding that monomer to the chain.

Azo-bis-cyclohexanoic carbonitrile is the photosensitive initiator which they have chosen. They have worked with butyl acrylate and styrene and acrylonitrile and styrene. The problems of separating homopolymers and copolymers from block polymers have not all been completely solved, but Melville and his associates have more nearly achieved their goal than has any other group working on block vinyl polymers.

Coleman [64] has been working on condensation block polymers, and his results indicate the trends and possibilities in this type of program. He has condensed dimethyl terephthalate, ethylene glycol, and polyethylene glycol in various ratios to get polymers which contain block segments of

$$-(OCH_2CH_2-)_n$$

in polyethylene terephthalate chains. He used polyethylene glycols with molecular weights of 1350 and 2800 in his work. The introduction of the new segment makes marked changes in solubility, dye receptivity, moisture regain, and second order transition (glass) temperature, but it has little effect on the crystalline melting point of the polymer. The copolymers differ markedly from a melt blend of polyethylene terephthalate and polyethylene glycol since these two polymers are incompatible in a mixture.

Angier, Ceresa, and Watson [65] have described experiments on the preparation of block polymers by masticating polymers in the rubbery state with monomers and thus causing polymerization of the new monomer. Block polymers of styrene and methyl methacrylate with relatively few segments of the source polymer were obtained.

[63] E. J. Dunn, B. D. Stead, and H. W. Melville, *Trans. Faraday Soc.*, **50**, 279 (1954); E. J. Dunn and H. W. Melville, *Nature*, **169**, 699 (1952); J. A. Hicks and H. W. Melville, *J. Polymer Sci.*, **12**, 461 (1954); H. W. Melville and B. D. Stead, *ibid.*, **16**, 505 (1955).

[64] D. Coleman, *J. Polymer Sci.*, **14**, 15 (1954).

[65] D. J. Angier, R. J. Ceresa, and W. F. Watson, International High Polymer Conference, Nottingham, England, July 21–24, 1958.

The whole field of block polymers will undoubtedly receive more and more attention as new methods of preparation are developed.

Graft Copolymers [62]

Graft copolymers are polymers in which a polymeric chain of one type of monomer is grafted on as a side chain to the backbone chain of another linear polymer. It represents another possible isomeric arrangement of units of monomers A and B in a polymer chain.

Here again the details of the changes in properties which graft polymers may produce are not well described. It is evident, however, that new properties will be found in such substances.

Houtz and Adkins [66] had previously grown polystyrene chains on a preformed polystyrene, but the idea of grafts was not clearly understood then. Carlin [67] mixed together p-chlorostyrene and polymethyl acrylate and added benzoyl peroxide. Chain transfer between radicals and polymethyl acrylate provided centers from which p-chlorostyrene polymer chains grew. Unusual solubility differences between

the two pure polymers and the graft polymer enabled separations to be made.

[66] R. C. Houtz and H. Adkins, *J. Am. Chem. Soc.*, **55**, 1609 (1933).

[67] R. B. Carlin and N. E. Shakespeare, *J. Am. Chem. Soc.*, **68**, 876 (1946).

Roland and Richards [68] have prepared graft polymers from a polyvinyl acetate backbone and grafted chains of polyethylene. Hydrolysis of the graft polymer showed that the ethylene polymer had grown mainly off the acetate methyl group. However, some chains had started from the backbone carbon chain.

Smets [69] has also worked on graft polymers, using polymethyl methacrylate and vinyl chloride, polyvinyl chloride and methyl methacrylate, etc. Solubility differences showed up markedly. Not all combinations tried gave graft polymers.

Graft polymers received extensive treatment at the International High Polymer Conference in Nottingham (July 21–24, 1958). A. S. Hoffman of Massachusetts Institute of Technology described the grafting of styrene onto low pressure polyethylene fibers by irradiation with cobalt-60 as the initiation method. A. A. Berlin (Moscow) discussed graft polymers prepared by polymerizing vinyl chloride in the presence of latices of a copolymer of butyl methacrylate and methacrylic acid. The properties of such graft polymers were different from the blends of similar polymers of vinyl chloride or the copolymer of butyl methacrylate and acrylic acid.

Radiation methods of producing graft polymers received especial treatment at this conference. It was shown that certain of these graft copolymers have much better compatibilities and solubilities than do mixtures of homopolymers. This whole field is an expanding one that needs further clarification and new techniques to open up all its possibilities.

Styrenated Polyesters

Styrenated polyesters, developed in recent years, are very important additions to the laminating industry. The copolymer is a combination of a condensation polymer and an addition polymer.

Polyester resins are prepared from dibasic acids and glycols. Some of the dibasic acid is unsaturated (maleic or fumaric), so the final polyester has some active olefinic group embedded in the chain. Styrene is now introduced into the polyester, the material molded to the desired shape, and the mixture heated to set off a heat-sensitive initiator which starts the styrene polymerizing. In its growth it incor-

[68] J. R. Roland and L. M. Richards, *J. Polymer Sci.*, **9**, 61 (1952).
[69] G. Smets and M. Claeson, *J. Polymer Sci.*, **8**, 289 (1952).

porates the maleic ester double bonds in the chain and thus crosslinks the polyester.

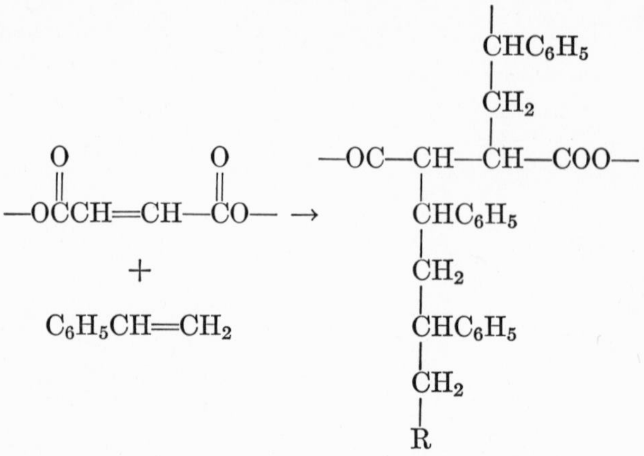

$$
\begin{array}{ccc}
 & & \overset{|}{C}HC_6H_5 \\
 & & \overset{|}{C}H_2 \\
O \qquad\qquad O & & \overset{|}{} \\
\parallel \qquad\qquad \parallel & & -OC-CH-\overset{|}{C}H-COO- \\
-O\overset{}{C}CH{=}CH-\overset{}{C}O- \rightarrow & & \overset{|}{C}HC_6H_5 \\
 & & \overset{|}{C}H_2 \\
+ & & \overset{|}{C}HC_6H_5 \\
C_6H_5CH{=}CH_2 & & \overset{|}{C}H_2 \\
 & & \overset{|}{R}
\end{array}
$$

Many variations and combinations are used to get the properties desired.

Diene Polymerization

Diene polymerization is being considered separately because structural problems increase with the increased possibilities for isomerism in these polymeric molecules.

The 1,3-dienes are the most important practical diene monomers, and in this group butadiene, isoprene, and chloroprene have been most widely studied. These dienes polymerize with all three standard types of initiation. They copolymerize with a very wide variety of monomers. The conditions used in polymerizing the monomer have a great deal to do with the structure of the polymer. These factors will be briefly considered.

Free Radical Initiated Polymerization

Dienes are readily polymerized with any free radical initiator, especially in emulsion systems. The rate of polymerization is determined by the diene and by the exact system used since these determine the initiation rate. Soap emulsions of butadiene can be polymerized at 0° in a few minutes under the most favorable conditions of initiation, or the process may require as many hours at 50° to obtain the same conversion under other conditions. Thus with persulfate-mercaptan initiation the time required to reach 60 to 70% conversions is about 12 to 14 hours at 50°. With an active redox system, using a highly oil soluble catalyst and a good complexing agent, the reaction has been carried out in 14 minutes at 0°. All variations in between are possible.

In making a polymer or copolymer of butadiene or isoprene which is to have useful properties as a synthetic elastomer, it is necessary to add a modifier or chain transfer agent to control the molecular weight and degree of branching of the polymer. In soap emulsion systems, this is usually lauryl mercaptan or some closely related mercaptan with the correct solubility in oil and water to ensure that the modifier is at the locus of polymerization in the right concentration to give the desired effect.

When a simple 1,3-diene such as butadiene is attacked by a free radical, two possible resonating structures result.

$$M \cdot + CH_2 = CH - CH = CH_2 \rightarrow$$

$$\overset{1}{M}CH_2\overset{2}{C}H = \overset{3}{C}H\overset{4}{C}H_2 \cdot \; \rightleftharpoons \; \overset{1}{M}CH_2\overset{2}{\underset{\cdot}{C}}H - \overset{3}{C}H = \overset{4}{C}H_2$$

The next unit of butadiene may be added at either the 2- or the 4-position with respect to M. The 1,2-adduct leaves a vinyl side chain; the 1,4-adduct introduces an ethylenic bond in the chain, and this may assume either a *cis* or a *trans* structure.

In the case of butadiene these two structures (1,2- and 1,4-) are produced at a nearly constant ratio under a very wide variety of conditions including temperature, and the polymer formed always has 78 to 82% 1,4-units and 22 to 18% 1,2-units in its structure. The ratio of *cis* to *trans* 1,4-units is affected by temperature. At −20° the 1,4-structural units are 78% *trans*, whereas at +100° they are only 40% *trans*.

When isoprene is polymerized in free radical systems even more structural isomers are possible in the polymer.

$$M\cdot + CH_2\!\!=\!\!\overset{\overset{\displaystyle CH_3}{|}}{C}\!\!-\!\!CH\!\!=\!\!CH_2 \;\rightarrow\; M\!\!-\!\!CH_2\!\!-\!\!\overset{\overset{\displaystyle CH_3}{|}}{C}\!\!=\!\!CH\!\!-\!\!CH_2\cdot \qquad (cis\ or\ trans)$$

$$\rightarrow\; M\!\!-\!\!CH_2\!\!-\!\!\overset{\overset{\displaystyle CH_3}{|}}{\underset{\cdot}{C}}\!\!-\!\!CH\!\!=\!\!CH_2$$

$$\rightarrow\; M\!\!-\!\!CH_2\!\!-\!\!CH\!\!=\!\!\overset{}{\underset{\underset{\displaystyle CH_3}{|}}{C}}\!\!-\!\!CH_2\cdot \qquad (cis\ or\ trans)$$

$$\rightarrow\; M\!\!-\!\!CH_2\!\!-\!\!\overset{}{\underset{}{\dot{C}H}}\!\!-\!\!\overset{\overset{\displaystyle CH_3}{|}}{C}\!\!=\!\!CH_2$$

Further addition of isoprene units makes possible two vinyl side chains (a and b) as well as *cis* and *trans* 1,4-adducts.

$$
-CH_2\!-\!\overset{\overset{\displaystyle CH_3}{|}}{\underset{\underset{\underset{\displaystyle CH_2}{\|}}{CH}}{C}}\!-\qquad\text{and}\qquad -CH_2\!-\!\overset{}{\underset{\underset{\underset{\displaystyle CH_2}{\|}}{C-CH_3}}{CH}}\!-
$$

(a)   (b)

In the case of isoprene there appears to be about 5 to 7% of each of these vinyl side chain units, the remaining about 85%+ being 1,4-adduct. At 0° these 1,4-units are about 10% *cis* and 90% *trans*, and at 100° the ratio is 30% *cis* to 70% *trans*.

Chloroprene, $CH_2\!\!=\!\!CCl\!\!-\!\!CH\!\!=\!\!CH_2$, polymerizes with ease to give 97% 1,4-units which seem to be predominantly *trans*.

2,3-Dimethylbutadiene yields at least 90% 1,4-units. Large alkyl groups in the 1,3-position increase the amount of 1,4-units. 2-Methyl-3-*n*-butylbutadiene gives a polymer which has at least 97% of its units in the 1,4-arrangement as determined by benzoyl hydroperoxide titration.

Ionic Initiated Polymerization of Dienes

Cationic polymerization of butadiene is not a very satisfactory procedure to give soluble polymers, because the addition of an active $-CH_2-$ group to a $-\overset{|}{C}\!\!=\!\!\overset{|}{C}-$ can arise and then crosslinking occurs. When low molecular weight polymers are produced, they seem to have considerable *trans* 1,4-structure.

A considerable amount of work has been done on sodium polymerization of butadiene, and the newer Alfin catalyst technique of Morton is probably a related ionic polymerization. Sodium induced polymers are certainly of different structure from those produced by free radical initiation. Also there is a marked effect of temperature on the ratio of 1,2- and 1,4-units in the ionic polymerization which does not occur in free radical polymerizations. Sodium at 50° gives a polymer from butadiene with as much as 59% 1,2-units. Ziegler claims that at lower temperatures even more of the material has the 1,2-structure and at higher temperatures there are more 1,4-units.

The case with polyisoprene is interesting because sodium gives 50% 1,4-units at 50° and these are mainly *trans*. Increasing the temperature of polymerization increases the 1,4-structure. Changing the metal also has a profound effect. Firestone Tire and Rubber Company has announced lithium metal polymerization of isoprene which yields 93% 1,4- and *cis*-polyisoprene which is very nearly identical with natural rubber.[70] The remainder of the polymer apparently has 3,4-addition units since no 1,2-units can be detected.

Natta has prepared poly-1,4-butadienes with both the *cis* and the *trans* configurations.[53, 71] In addition he has reported the 1,2-polybutadienes which are syndiotactic and isotactic.[72] Phillips Petroleum Company has also described stereospecific polybutadienes prepared by their catalytic process.[73]

The Alfin catalyst of Morton is prepared by converting amyl sodium to sodium allyl and adding an exact molecular equivalent of sodium isopropoxide. The amyl sodium is prepared from amyl chloride and sodium, and it appears that the by-product, sodium chloride, is an important part of this heterogeneous catalyst system. When prepared properly, this is an extremely active initiator of butadiene polymerization, and polybutadiene of extremely high molecular weight is produced in seconds at room temperature.

Morton believes that the Alfin catalyst is a free radical initiator and cites the fact that the 1,2:1,4 ratio of polymer structural units falls in the same ratio that they do in free radical initiated polymers.

[70] *Chem. Eng. News,* **35,** 3716 (Sept. 5, 1955).

[71] G. Natta, *Angew. Chem.,* **68,** 393 (1956).

[72] G. Natta, *Modern Plastics,* **34,** 169 (1956); *Chim. e ind. (Milan),* **39,** 653 (1957); *Chim. & ind. (Paris),* **77,** 1009 (1957); *Experientia Suppl.,* **No. 7,** 21 (1957).

[73] Phillips Petroleum Company, Belgian Patent 551,851 (1956).

Diem,[74] in the Goodrich laboratory, has carried out copolymerization experiments of styrene and methyl methacrylate and concluded that the Alfin catalyst gives the same composition of copolymer (99% methyl methacrylate, 1% styrene) as do anionic catalysts. A free radical catalyst in the same monomer composition leads to a copolymer with 51% styrene. He also obtained evidence that the copolymerization of butadiene and styrene gave copolymer composition more in keeping with anionic than with free radical initiation.

It probably is best to be somewhat open-minded on the question at this stage. The anionic mechanism seems more probable, but the final answer has not yet been established beyond doubt.

Diene Copolymers

A butadiene-styrene copolymer made in a free radical system is current GR-S, Government rubber styrene type. It is composed of about 75% by weight of butadiene and 25% by weight of styrene units. The butadiene segment has the same general arrangement of diene units as polybutadiene itself (1,2-, 1,4-*cis* and *trans*). When prepared at lower temperatures (0°), the polymer is less branched and more narrow in molecular weight distribution than is the 50° polymer. This makes the product a better synthetic rubber for tread stock.

GR-S is not a good carcass stock rubber because it has a high heat build-up in operation. The new lithium metal polyisoprene of Firestone and the Ziegler catalyzed polyisoprene of Goodrich overcome this problem and give good carcass stock polymers.

Butadiene (and the other dienes) copolymerize very readily with a wide variety of other monomers. These copolymers have been studied extensively as possible substitutes for GR-S. It is apparent that the general tensile properties, heat build-up, etc., are about the same for all butadiene copolymers regardless of the comonomer used. However, the comonomer is important in determining solvent resistance, freeze point, and other properties of that type.

Butyl rubber is an isobutylene-butadiene (or isoprene) copolymer made in a cationic initiation system. Only a small percentage of diene is used, and that is needed for the vulcanization of the butyl rubber. Butyl rubber is a copolymer with many superior properties. It is especially resistant to oxidation, and as the vulcanized film it has excellent properties for holding gas pressure in such items as inner tubes.

[74] H. E. Diem, CR-3781 (April 29, 1955) (The B. F. Goodrich Company).

Non-conjugated Dienes

Diolefins which have no conjugated structures and no activating groups usually do not undergo polymerization reactions to any appreciable extent. They act only as diluents for a system which has groups present that may polymerize. Sometimes they are active inhibitors of polymerization if the unsaturation is so situated as to produce an active methylene type of structure.

Thus cyclopentadiene, divinylmethane, and other molecules with structures of that type are active inhibitors in free radical initiated polymerizations. 1,4-Cyclohexadiene and indene are likewise inhibitors in radical reactions. It should be noted that such molecules may polymerize in ionic systems.

Diolefins such as divinyl benzene [75] (o, m, p), divinyl esters of dibasic acids, glycol esters of acrylic acids, etc., in which two double bonds of a polymerizable type are present, are crosslinking agents. Both groups enter into the reaction, and the polymers become insoluble and infusible. Such network-forming monomers are sometimes added deliberately in small amounts to introduce their effects to a limited degree.

One interesting example of the effects of two or more vinyl groups has been reported by Butler. Allyl compounds, $CH_2\!=\!CH\!-\!CH_2\!-$, usually do not polymerize well. But diallyl diethylammonium bromide has been found to yield low polymers which are quite soluble, whereas the triallylamine derivative gives crosslinked insoluble polymers. The suggestion was made that the diallylamine derivative polymerizes in such a way that the two vinyl groups interact to produce rings.

This structure has now been well established.[76] Holt and Simpson [77] have also called attention to the fact that cyclization accompanies

---

[75] H. Staudinger and W. Heuer, *Ber.*, **67**, 1159 (1934).

[76] G. B. Butler and R. J. Angelo, *J. Am. Chem. Soc.*, **79**, 3128 (1957); G. B. Butler, A. Crawshaw, and W. L. Miller, *ibid.*, **80**, 3615 (1958).

[77] T. Holt and W. Simpson, *Proc. Roy. Soc.* (*London*), **A238**, 154 (1956).

chain polymerization and crosslinking during the free radical polymerization of diallyl esters of dibasic acids.

This intramolecular-intermolecular type of polymerization has also been demonstrated for dimethyl α,α'-dimethylenepimelate [78] in a free radical initiated reaction and for 1,6-heptadiene [79] in a Ziegler type polymerization. In both of these cases the presence of the six-mem-

bered carbocyclic ring in the polymer chain was demonstrated by dehydrogenation to yield a polymer containing aromatic structures which were demonstrated by ultraviolet and infrared absorption spectra.

When other α,ω-diolefins were examined in this type of polymerization some cyclization was achieved, but considerable open chain monoölefin links were also present and no high polymeric material could be produced without extensive crosslinking.[80]

It has been mentioned earlier that 1,3-butadiene polymers and copolymers are usually prepared in the presence of a chain transfer agent (modifier) to give soluble products. The insolubility is undoubtedly produced here by the entry of the polybutadiene, a multifunctional

[78] C. S. Marvel and R. D. Vest, *J. Am. Chem. Soc.*, **79**, 5771 (1957).

[79] C. S. Marvel and J. K. Stille, *J. Am. Chem. Soc.*, **80**, 1740 (1958).

[80] C. S. Marvel and W. E. Garrison, *J. Am. Chem. Soc.*, in press.

olefin, into further chain growth through its double bonds to give a crosslinked polymer. This further growth may involve the double unions of the 1,4-diene units or of the 1,2-diene units in the polymer chain. No evidence has been produced to establish which is involved.

$$-CH_2-CH=CH-CH_2- \rightarrow \begin{array}{c} -CH_2-CH-CH-CH_2 \\ | \\ -CH_2-CH=CHCH_2 \end{array}$$

$$\begin{array}{c} -CH_2-CH- \\ | \\ CH \\ \| \\ CH_2 \end{array} \rightarrow \begin{array}{c} -CH_2-CH- \\ | \\ CH- \\ | \\ -CH_2-CH=CHCH_2-CH_2 \end{array}$$

It has been found that the amount of branching or crosslinking of this type is related to the amount of monomer and polymer in the system. At the beginning of polymerizations with high monomer concentration, little or no branching occurs. At about 30% conversion the branching operation becomes serious, and unless the chain transfer agent is present soluble polymers cannot be obtained much above this conversion. If the chain transfer agent is present, the conversion can be carried up to about 60 to 70%. After that amount of polymer is present, even chain transfer agents do not seem to prevent crosslinking completely unless they are in such high concentration that only extremely short chains are produced.

Reactions of Polymers

The functional groups in polymers have the same general ease of reaction as they have in monomeric molecules. This has an important bearing upon their stability (particularly of condensation polymers) and also makes possible chemical transformations which will change the properties of the polymer in a desired manner.

Probably the most important factor in connection with polymer reactions is the physical state of the polymer and the manner in which it may influence the collisions between reagent and the groups with which it must react to bring about a reaction. Steric interference is usually enhanced in polymers. Interchain attractions which are strongly exhibited in highly crystalline polymers are extremely important factors in reactivity. However, reactions do occur readily as evidenced by the fact that condensation polymers form at a finite rate, demonstrating that the end groups maintain their activity as the chain lengthens.

The methods used to determine end groups in a condensation polymer such as nylon show that terminal amine and carboxyl groups are still active, for they may be titrated with acid or base as the case may be. The preparation of a solution of the polymer and a common solvent for the titrating reagent often becomes the major problem in such determinations.

One of the best-known sequences of polymer reactions is probably that of changing polyvinyl acetate to a polyacetal. This reaction is

interesting because it brings out a point stressed by Flory,[31] namely, that in a chain such as polyvinyl alcohol which has groups that may react in pairs, some of these groups should become isolated by chance during such a reaction. Statistically the groups isolated should amount to 13.5% of the total. It is significant that, if acetalization of polyvinyl alcohol is carried to more than 85%, crosslinking begins to set in and insolubility appears. This means that the isolated hydroxyl groups are then reacting to form acetals which crosslink one chain to the next. There are many examples of this isolation of reactive groups in such pairing reactions.

Evidence has been obtained that metals act on polyvinyl chloride to remove chlorine and yield cyclopropane structures. Here again some chlorine atoms (about 14%) became isolated.[81]

Polymethyl acrylate can be hydrolyzed to polyacrylic acid and converted to polyacrylamide by the action of ammonia, just as any ester gives these reactions. Polymethyl methacrylate is extremely inert. This seems to be due entirely to steric effects. The polyacrylate ester (I) is like a monomeric ester of a disubstituted acetic acid which can be hydrolyzed. The polymethacrylate ester (II) is a trisubstituted

$$\left(CH_2-\underset{\underset{CO_2CH_3}{|}}{CH}-CH_2-\underset{\underset{CO_2CH_3}{|}}{CH}\right)_n \qquad \left(CH-\underset{\underset{CO_2CH_3}{|}}{\overset{\overset{CH_3}{|}}{C}}-CH_2-\underset{\underset{CO_2CH_3}{|}}{\overset{\overset{CH_3}{|}}{C}}\right)_n$$

I   II

acid ester which is not easily hydrolyzed in the monomeric types, and the polymer structure enhances the hindrance to hydrolytic change.

An important property of linear polyesters is their stability or lack of stability to hydrolysis. In general, soluble linear polyesters hydrolyze with ease and this severely limits their use. Many polyesters would make good synthetic fibers except for this fact. Polyethylene terephthalate has such low solubility that water does not seem to get to the necessary reaction site to produce rapid hydrolysis at ordinary temperatures. The alkyds, laminating esters, and other practical polyesters of that sort are generally crosslinked to a sufficient extent to reduce their water sensitivity and thus give them the needed stability under most conditions of use.

A reaction which has increased in importance in recent years is the nitration and reduction of styrene polymers and copolymers. This leads to important basic resins used in ion exchange applications. Sulfonation of styrene polymers leads to strong polyacids. The ion exchange resins are either polyacids, polybases, or combinations of them. They have achieved great importance in demineralizing water for industrial applications. Ordinary water can be converted to water sufficiently pure for conductivity work by use of ion exchange resins. Such resins have almost completely taken the place of water stills to furnish "distilled" water for laboratory and industrial uses.

The acetylation, nitration, and xanthation of cellulose are important reactions of natural polymers. Crosslinking natural polymers to make plastics and fibers is another example of reactions of polymers.

[81] C. S. Marvel, J. H. Sample, and M. F. Roy, *J. Am. Chem. Soc.*, **61**, 3241 (1939).

The hydrochlorination of natural rubber and the vulcanization of rubber are useful polymer reactions of common application.

$$\left(\!\!\begin{array}{c} CH_3 \\ | \\ CH_2-C=CH-CH_2 \end{array}\!\!\right)_{\!n} \xrightarrow{\ HCl\ } \left(\!\!\begin{array}{c} CH_3 \\ | \\ CH_2-C-CH_2\,CH_2 \\ | \\ Cl \end{array}\!\!\right)$$

Vulcanization is the more complex reaction, and the exact mechanism is not yet entirely settled. It undoubtedly involves first an attack on the allylic CH_2 by the sulfur to give either an —S—SH or —SH group. This in turn reacts with the double bond of a neighboring chain to yield a crosslink which is either an —S—S— or —S— bond. It is likely that both types of crosslinks occur.

Teyssié and Smets [82] have shown that polyvinyl chloride can be used as the halide component in a Friedel-Crafts type of reaction with such hydrocarbons as benzene, toluene, *m*-xylene, pseudocumene, and mesitylene. With benzene they had hoped to achieve a polymer such as might be expected by the copolymerization of styrene and vinyl chloride. These two monomers have reactivity ratios which are extremely unfavorable for copolymerization. The reaction, however, went one step further to give cyclization to a 1,3-indane derivative.

Some successful lithium aluminum hydride reactions of butadiene-

[82] Ph. Teyssié and G. Smets, *J. Polymer Sci.*, **20**, 351 (1956).

methyl acrylate copolymers yield butadiene-allyl alcohol copolymers.[83]

Many more such cases are coming to our attention each year. Again it should be noted that such reactions are primarily limited by considerations of solubility and by the possibilities of innumerable side reactions.

[83] C. S. Marvel, R. M. Potts, and Charles King, *J. Am. Chem. Soc.,* **77,** 177 (1955).

Index